33162

THE CONVERTS

Following his two much-praised Julius Caesar novels Rex Warner has written a fascinating reconstruction of the early life of St Augustine in fourth-century Rome and Milan.

It is a brilliant portrait of a complicated man, set in a time of political decadence but also of intellectual and religious ferment. Traditional ways of government, of life, of religion and of thought were changing rapidly and decisively. Christianity, though already given official backing by the Emperor Constantine, was still challenged by other creeds and continually in process of defining itself.

Augustine's moral and intellectual growing pains are described through the imagined journal of Alypius, his greatest friend and admirer. After they have studied together in Carthage Augustine rejoins Alypius in Rome, where they are immediately caught up in the struggle of contemporary philosophies.

Rex Warner involves us deeply in moral and social issues which are as relevant today as they were in Augustine's time. As always his prose is vivid and athletic and his historical touch accurate and wholly convincing.

By the same author

NOVELS
The Wild Goose Chase
The Professor
The Aerodrome
Why Was I Killed?
Men of Stones
Escapade
The Young Caesar
Imperial Caesar
Pericles the Athenian

MYTHOLOGY
Men and Gods
Greeks and Trojans
The Vengeance of the Gods

TRANSLATIONS
The Medea of Euripides
The Prometheus Bound of Aeschylus

POETRY
Poems and Contradictions

ESSAYS
The Cult of Power

TRAVEL
Views of Attica

REX WARNER
The Converts

a novel of
Early Christianity

THE BODLEY HEAD
LONDON SYDNEY
TORONTO

© Rex Warner 1967
Printed and bound in Great Britain for
The Bodley Head Ltd
9 Bow Street, London, WC2
by William Clowes & Sons Ltd, Beccles
Set in Monotype Imprint
First published 1967

To
George Seferis

CONTENTS

Part One, 1

Part Two, 115

Part Three, 197

*part
one*

I

I am very young, indeed only twenty-one years old, and it is quite certain that many of my observations are inexact, many of my views mistaken. Nevertheless, now that I am alone in Rome, I shall from time to time write down my thoughts, rather for my own benefit than for that of anyone else. When I was in Africa I would share my thoughts with my friends and they theirs with me—that was the greatest happiness I have known, and the others, too, were happy. I think of those days with the pain of regret, but also with gratitude and somehow an assurance that they are not over, but will come again. True that Augustine and Nebridius are still in Carthage; but Augustine has already talked of coming to Rome, where I know he would soon become famous; and Nebridius is rich enough to travel wherever he likes. So I shall not always have to think of my friends in absence; over here we shall be able to meet and to walk out into the country and share our feelings as we did in Thagaste and in Carthage.

It is indolent perhaps of me to spend so much time in thinking of my friends and of the pleasure we all found in each other's company. I have much work to do in my law studies and much more work to do in the pursuit of wisdom, to which we have all pledged ourselves. Though I am reasonably well read in literature, my knowledge of astronomy is very limited, and, more important, I find it quite impossible to understand or even with any confidence to conjecture the nature of God. Nor is it much relief to me to discover that nearly everyone else seems to be in the same predicament. There seem to be as many Gods as there are men, and many of these Gods, like that of the Christians, seem capable of

3

endless or at least triple subdivisions. This is disturbing for a young man, and there is no easy way to test, by moral or aesthetic standards, the beliefs of others. Some of the Christians are fools and hypocrites; others, like Augustine's mother, seem to have every virtue—though it may be that Monnica does have a too fierce and almost oppressive affection for her son. Some of those who worship the old Gods are men of admirable behaviour, great learning, a fine public spirit—like our friend Volusianus in Africa or that great old noble I met the other day, Praetextatus. Others have all the vices satirized by Juvenal and Persius. I myself am able to be neither good nor wise and though it would help me to become better and wiser if I could reach some definite conclusion about the nature of the world in which I live, I have reached no conclusion that means very much to me. There is a certain charm about the doctrines of the Manichees, especially when they are expounded by Augustine; but even he is not wholly convinced by them. He shows no wish, for instance, to become one of the 'perfect', and, with his vehement and honest personality, he would desire this if he were completely satisfied with their teachings. He says that his decision to remain a 'hearer' is a weak one and proceeds simply from his inability to go without the pleasures of sexual love. He is not yet fit for chastity, he thinks, and he supposes that in his nature the elements of darkness (for which, of course, he is not responsible, since they were part of his nature from birth) are still so glutinously blended with the seeds of light that he is unable to reach the sanctity required of those who neither take life in the form of food nor produce life by sexual intercourse. In this respect he has often contrasted his way of life with mine. According to him, I am happy because I live chastely.

I do not find this view of his at all convincing. In the first place my chastity does not proceed from any virtue that I can acknowledge in myself. The fact is that I am rather disgusted by women when looked at as objects of physical desire. This may be due either to a deficiency in my nature or to that ex-

4

perience, the memory of which still makes me blush for shame, which I had when I was a schoolboy at Madaura. In the second place, I am not happy. Often when I look at Augustine and his mistress and their little son Adeodatus, I feel a loving sympathy for them which makes me sad in the thought that I am missing something of great value. They seem to me to share together in something finer than the mere enjoyment of their frequent love-making—friendship, I mean, divided responsibility and a bond of affection that appears to me more worthy than the refined enthusiasm of the Manichaean 'perfect', many of whom are not, in fact, at all averse from pleasure and find what seems to me a perverted satisfaction in their intellectual conviction that they can indulge innocently in the delights of sex, so long as these do not result in the physical bearing of children.

It is all very confusing, and I wonder whether there was ever a time when a young man with any philosophical aspirations has not been confused. In our education we are encouraged to admire those characters from the distant past who are said to have followed unerringly and with perfect conviction the right paths of duty, thought and behaviour. But I doubt whether these people ever existed except in history books. Many of them gave up their lives for their ideals, but is this in itself admirable? The Donatists in Africa are only too apt to do this. They will actually provoke their enemies or the civil authorities to kill them simply in order to secure the distinction of martyrdom and are impervious to any argument that might convince them that they may be sacrificing their lives for a mistaken or unimportant theoretical view. One may say, I suppose, that they have certainty; yet still their minds lack clarity. And when, as our education proceeds, we come to the study of the poets and philosophers, we find every kind of doubt, hesitation and diversity. We are indeed moved by Virgil, but what moves us is (apart from the beauty of language and versification) the discovery that even he was in this world often as limited and unhappy as ourselves. Sophocles, the most beautiful and gentlest man of his age, famous throughout his life, a friend of the great, confesses that what is most desirable is never to have been born.

I myself am not sorry that I have been born, but I am frightened to find myself where I am and I am bewildered when I observe how few others share my apprehension and my distress. That is one reason why I miss my friends; for we all, in one way or another, long to know the reason and the meaning of our existence and cannot be satisfied with what appears to us as the cynicism of our elders, who will blandly, and even happily, inform us that no reason can be determined and no meaning discovered. If that were so, I should be terrified, and not filled with awe, when I look up at the stars. Even now I am sometimes terrified at the thought of the bodies of women and of men, though not, curiously enough, by the bodies of animals or of birds.

I would like all things to be pure, beautiful and friendly; but I am not pure myself. If I were, I should never have gone to that place in Madaura, nor should I have delighted with such mad frenzy in the sight of blood in the arena. I have felt purity and understanding in the society of my friends; but not elsewhere. No doubt, as the Manichees say, we are compounded of Light and Darkness. I am in the dark.

II

I recall the entertainment which I enjoyed two days ago at the house of Vettius Agorius Praetextatus. When one of his slaves brought me the invitation I was amused to notice the effect on

the landlord of the apartment which I now rent. This landlord is a freedman. He came originally, I think, from Syria
and speaks Greek better than Latin. He seems to me a very
old man, though he is probably under sixty. He is voluble,
like most of his race, and whenever I give him the slightest
opportunity he will speak at great length about Antioch,
which he claims to be a more beautiful city than Rome, filled
with orators, clergy and poets more distinguished than any to
be found in the west. When I tell him that we in Africa are
inferior to none in oratory, literature and poetry or attempt
to describe to him the beauties and splendour of Carthage, he
is wholly incredulous and changes the subject at once, as
though he were dealing with a madman. I did, I think, impress him slightly with my knowledge of philosophy, which,
though small, is greater than his own; but he soon regained
any ground he might have imagined that he had lost by displaying a far more thorough acquaintance than I can boast of
with the intricacies of religious controversy in the eastern
Christian Church. He is a passionate adherent of any argument or textual interpretation which seems to indicate that
the Son, while fully God, is somehow rather less fully God
than is the Father. I soon observed that his fervour on this
subject has nothing to do with any desire for the truth or even
for the living of a good life. He is concerned simply to back
his fancy and is at least as enthusiastic about these logical
subtleties as any of us might be in arguing about the style or
methods of a favourite charioteer in the circus. When I told
him that my mother is a Christian and my father is not, he
showed not the slightest interest; nor is he at all devoted to
this religion himself. He despises the monks and hermits, of
whom there seem to be as many in the East as there are said
to be in Egypt, and he admitted that when Julian was emperor, he abandoned for a short time the religion in which he
had been brought up. However, Julian appears to have made
himself unpopular in Antioch, where the people laughed at
his beard, and this fact was sufficient to reconvert my land-

lord, who was then in the East, to Christianity. He reminds me of a schoolmaster we used to have in Madaura, who was far more interested in combinations of grammatical devices than in any sense expressed by the works he used. This schoolmaster disliked me intensely, but he disliked Augustine even more, since Augustine was better able than I was to expose the real ignorance of the man. He frequently had us beaten in those days, though now, if we ever see him, he treats us (and particularly Augustine) with the greatest respect and claims to be responsible for what he calls our success. I try, if I can, to be polite to everyone, but I find it difficult to conceal my contempt for hypocrisy. That is why, I suppose, my landlord regards me as being peculiarly stupid.

I should have said 'regarded', since he now looks upon me with an extraordinary respect and has even offered me a better room in his house for no additional rent. I did not immediately understand the reason for this sudden change in his attitude. Soon I discovered that it was entirely determined by snobbery, which is, of course, a habit of many minds, though one which I find difficult to understand. It seems to me preposterous to imagine that simply because one is acquainted with a man who is good, wise or rich one becomes in oneself either better, wiser or richer. However, this is certainly the belief of my landlord. The fact that I have a slight acquaintanceship with Praetextatus has suddenly made me appear to him as a superior being to what I was yesterday; and, even more remarkable, he has decided that he also has increased in importance.

It is, of course, natural to be impressed by magnificence. Wealth, power, an honoured name and a distinguished career are all to be admired, and I have observed that those who have a tendency to belittle these things are usually actuated by a mean type of envy which is much more disgusting than the absurdities of my landlord, though both the envy and the unreasoned adulation seem to spring from the same source—

8

a desire to convince oneself that one is better than one is. And even those who are themselves individually great and powerful seem liable to take pleasure in the flattery of others who are inferior to them. Such pleasure must conceal an inner weakness and insecurity. Perhaps there is no one who is happy.

In all my little experience I should say that Praetextatus has the best titles to happiness and security. His family is of the highest importance and is bound together by close ties of affection and respect. He has himself filled many great offices including that of prefect of the City. He is a fine speaker, a scholar and a philosopher. He is both rich and handsome. His friends are numerous and sincere and his wife, to whom he has remained faithful throughout their long marriage, is as devoted to him as he is to her. Though he has passed middle age, he is strong and healthy, able to spend long hours in the hunting field or in the law courts or in philosophical discussion with his friends. Yet even he is not wholly at ease. It is not, I think, only his excellent manners that lead him to show interest in the ideas even of young men as ignorant as I am; it is because he too is unsatisfied and is seeking for a certainty which he does not in fact possess.

I was privileged to dine with Praetextatus and his wife alone and I shall always remember their kindness to me and the care they took to make me, a provincial new to Rome, feel at my ease. I had only met Praetextatus once or twice before and that was when he came to Africa to visit his friend Symmachus, who was then pro-consul of the province. They were entertained at Thagaste both by my father and by my rich kinsman Romanianus. My father regards my abilities very much more highly than they deserve, and, since Symmachus is known to be one of the greatest rhetoricians of the age, he was determined that I should impress the great man by declaiming some passage of Virgil. Both Symmachus and Praetextatus (as good manners required) congratulated me on my performance. I wished that Augustine had been there to take my place. His voice is less powerful than mine, but his sense of rhythm is more exact, and he can express a far greater range of emotion. However, Augustine was in Carthage and, even if he had been in Thagaste, my father would not have invited him. At this time, for no very good reason, he disapproved both of him and of our close friendship, though Romanianus, who is a great deal younger than my father, has always admired Augustine for his eager and vehement intelligence (which rather offends my father) and can recognize the sweetness of his character.

On this evening in Rome I met Praetextatus' wife Paulina for the first time. She is elderly, as he is, and, like him, tall and exceedingly handsome. She was dressed magnificently, I know, though I have always been bad at recalling precisely the colour, shape and texture of women's clothes. I remember her gold ear-rings, which seemed to be of Egyptian design, and a necklace, also Egyptian, of twined serpents. What most struck me was the size and depth of her eyes. They were particularly expressive and variable, sometimes appearing to go past one, engulfing or absorbing, sometimes concentrated like a steady beam of light. Her manner had the grace that comes from calm, and, I suppose, security; yet it was not the calm of the self-absorbed. Her sensitiveness was such that she seemed to understand one's mind before one had begun to express it in words.

The food was brought to us on golden and silver plate. It was good and plentiful, but simple and without any great number of courses. This pleased me, as I hate those banquets at which one has either to offend one's host by refusing to taste everything that is set before one or else to eat twice as much as one needs or desires. Praetextatus himself showed a healthy appetite, but his wife ate little except fruit and vegetables and drank not more than one cup of wine. As the evening went on she took more and more evident interest in the conversation. I noticed that when speaking she would often pick up from the table by her a small alabaster statue of

Isis. This she would hold between her hands, sometimes twining her fingers about it, sometimes letting it rest in her palm.

We began by talking of friends whom Praetextatus had met in Africa and, after mentioning my father and Romanianus, went on to speak of Publicius Albinus. This man, like Praetextatus a member of one of the greatest families in Rome, had long been a friend of both Praetextatus and his wife. They recalled the magnificence with which he had restored the capitol of Timgad in Africa and the large additional sums of money he had spent on dedicating a chapel to Mithra. As I seldom go to Timgad or have ever been particularly interested in the religion of Mithra, I was unable to reply very intelligently to the questions put to me on this subject. Praetextatus, with his excellent manners, was quick to put me at my ease. 'We would be most distressed,' he said, 'if by making these inquiries we are embarrassing you. I seem to remember that your father, like Albinus himself, worships the Gods, while your mother, like that good lady, Albinus' wife, is a Christian. You have not told me yet about your own views on this important subject. I can see however that you are a cultured and intelligent young man (that is clear from your knowledge of Virgil), and I cannot imagine that you, whatever your beliefs, can share in that fanatical intolerance and plain disregard for logic and experience which I observe in some Christians, though by no means in all. I have indeed many friends among the sect.'

'The women, I think,' said Paulina, 'are really more inhuman than the men. Or perhaps it is that they are easy subjects for that male fanaticism which we noticed the other day when we met that dreadful man (Jerome, is it not?) at Paula's home.'

Praetextatus smiled. 'I think I agree with your choice of words, my dear. All the same Jerome is a really great scholar. I believe him too to be sincere. He is even capable of showing excellent manners. Yet something seems to drive him into an irritable bearishness, and, as you say, his influence over those poor girls is thoroughly deplorable.' He turned to me. 'You will certainly know the family of which we are speaking. Young Volusianus' sister, Laeta, married into it. She too is a Christian, and so was her mother. This did not prevent her from living happily with Laeta's father, and I hope that Laeta too is happy with young Toxotius. He is a fine young man and of course worships the Gods of our country. Since he can trace his family back to Aeneas, that is only natural.'

He spoke these last words with a slight smile and I half wondered whether he, who was, I knew, one of the most learned men of the times, could really believe in these absurd stories, which Augustine, Nebridius and I had so often laughed about—that Aeneas, and the whole Julian house for that matter, had the Goddess Venus for their ancestress. As though there were not such an impassable gulf between what is divine and what is human. So easy and friendly were the manners of my hosts that I would have ventured to ask the question, if Paulina had not turned to me with further explanations of the family which they were discussing.

'I think Laeta is quite happy,' she said. 'It is her sisters-in-law who really cause us anxiety. And that is entirely due to that man Jerome, whom I shall continue to call dreadful.' Her large eyes rested for a moment on my face and I seemed to see in them an infinite kindness and generosity—something very different from the look of one great lady who is finding fault with another.

'You see,' she went on, 'young Toxotius' mother (the Paula of whom we are speaking) is a devout Christian and she has this Jerome as a spiritual adviser. He has persuaded the poor woman that all women should live and die virgins. As it happens one of the daughters, young Blaesilla, has just become a widow, and this monk actually congratulates her on her husband's death. It leaves her free, he says, to become the bride of Christ—a pleasure which seems to me quite devoid of meaning. In fact his language is often revoltingly coarse. And now he subjects the poor girls to the most appalling and even rather squalid tortures. They are not allowed to have a bath, for instance, and if they even look at a man, he tells them that they have done something impure.'

I am interested in this cult of virginity and so friendly was Paulina's manner that I ventured to ask her whether in her view there was anything wrong or impure in the virgin state.

'No, of course,' she said; 'there can be nothing wrong in the exercise of purity. Both my husband and I are used to the long periods of abstinence which must precede initiation into the mysteries. You cannot see God or Goddess without a pure heart and the purity of the body will help and even represent the purity of insight which we desire before the holy things are revealed to us. But these abstinences are for times which have been laid down by the priests and priestesses in their knowledge and experience of what cannot be described. There are also other sides of life. We can worship God and each other in the body as well as the soul. The life of the Gods is infinite and has more aspects than we shall ever discover. We may worship Isis, Ceres, Aphrodite, Hercules, Mithra in different ways, which are yet still the same way, since all these are aspects of one divine power.' She spoke with the utmost gravity and seriousness and in her expression and manner there was a grace and a warmth which seemed to me in themselves divine. I had been told that she, together with her husband, had been initiated into all the mysteries, was a priestess of many cults, yet the mother of a family, an admired type of what is assumed to have been the womanly virtue of the past and at the same time a woman of learning, startling beauty, kindness and affection. I saw that all this was true, and I admired her, I think, more than I have ever admired any woman, though all that she was saying conflicted with so many of the conclusions which I and my friends had tentatively been probing for in Africa. It was our habit to deride equally the rites to which she was so evidently devoted and the quaint superstitions of the Christians. Yet I saw that she was more content and perhaps wiser than we were. Again I wished that Augustine was here; he would not have been, like me, at a loss for something to say, though I think that he also would have been transported by the beauty and the sincerity of Paulina. Her expression had now changed and she was smiling at her husband. 'Agorius,' she said, 'I am talking too much, and very badly. All I meant to say was that I am sorry for that poor girl Blaesilla and for her sister Eustochium. I think the condition of Blaesilla is really dangerous. She is fasting continuously; she never sleeps; she is constantly ill. If her health should really collapse, it will be the fault of that dreadful man.'

Praetextatus nodded gravely in assent. 'I quite agree with you,' he said. 'But our young friend looks puzzled. Let us see what he thinks about all this.'

It was the kindness and dignity of his manner which prevented me from feeling more awkward and embarrassed than I did at the prospect of expressing my so ill-defined views before people much more learned and experienced than myself. 'If I may,' I said, 'I will speak frankly, since I am sure that you will recognize that I aim at discovering the truth and that, if I could believe them true, I should gladly share the convictions which you hold so sincerely. I can see and admire the purity of your lives; yet I cannot understand how that purity can be inculcated by the religious rites which I have often witnessed in Carthage and elsewhere. You know our great temple to the Heavenly Goddess, called sometimes Tanit (which is the old Punic name), sometimes Caelestis. We say that the temple was built by Dido before Aeneas came to Africa. Thus the Goddess must have come originally from Phoenicia and is no doubt associated with Astarte, the Syrian Goddess and, indeed, others. The statue in the temple is an almost shapeless stone female figure with arms raised. Often however the Goddess is represented as a virgin being carried by a lion. This seems to relate her with Cybele. Then too she is associated with Baal or Saturn, who is often represented by phalli or else by pillars representing the sun's rays. But no doubt you are better informed than I am in the details of the ceremonial. Can you explain why it is that I find it both intellectually absurd and morally disgusting? In the first place, how can a divine power exist in an almost shapeless stone? She is not even beautiful like the creations of the Greeks. Then how can a Goddess be both a virgin and not a virgin? But what most offends me is the nature of her worship. The temple is attended by organized troops of female prostitutes and many of these girls have been dedicated to the Goddess from birth. It is thought to be wrong if any of these refuse any man, however unsightly and bestial he may be. And in the religious processions they and the dancers and actors with them do everything possible to excite the lust of those who are watching them. How can these lascivious gestures, this public representation of acts that, if done at all, should be done in private be pleasing to the Gods whom we must believe to be higher and purer than we are? Are not these just the remains of the wantonness and superstition of an uncivilized past? In fact it was not so very long ago that our Gods were worshipped with human sacrifices. Even now when criminals are thrown to the wild beasts in the amphitheatre, the males are dressed as priests of Moloch or Saturn, and the females as priestesses of Ceres or Caelestis. And it is the same in Rome. You must know, I am sure, that I respect your own piety and look up to your superior learning; yet I cannot understand how you can bear to look at the obscene public ceremonies of the feast of Flora, or those castrated mincing priests of Attis, whose chief preoccupation seems to be to find elderly men to pay them for the use of their oiled repulsive bodies. I agree that the Christians believe a number of things that are incredible. How can a God suffer in human flesh, for instance? That, surely, is a plain contradiction. And it is true that many of the Christians behave like wild beasts or lunatics. You know of our Donatists in Africa, of how these misguided creatures, offending against the laws of God and man, will actually invite persecution in order to be able to call themselves martyrs, or else will go round the country in armed bands, killing the Catholics (whose religious tenets are in fact the same as theirs) or torturing them by throwing vitriol in their faces. It would seem impossible that anything good should exist among such madmen and bigots. And yet there are other facts which cannot be denied. The Christians will sacrifice money and time in helping those of their faith who are poor or sick; they not only profess but actually show, when they are not under the spell of theological fury, a forbearance, a moderation and a purity in their personal lives of which any philosopher must approve. They seem to act here with a kind of natural grace and simplicity and learn their manners not from any knowledge of philosophy, but from their faith itself, which cannot make many intellectual demands upon them except for an extraordinary credulity, but does make moral demands which appear to be good. I must own, for instance, that I sympathize with them when they denounce the sacrifices and obscene spectacles to which I have just referred. Forgive me if I appear to speak rudely and with too little restraint. It is simply that I am confused in my mind.'

I felt Paulina's eyes upon my face and was glad to see that her expression of kindness was unchanged. Praetextatus was leaning forward and I admired the strength and nobility of his features. He is more like what one was taught to imagine was the ancient Roman of the heroic times of the republic than anyone I have ever seen—a fine general and administrator, honest, robust and powerful; yet he has also other and to me even more attractive qualities, a sensitiveness to other minds, great intellectual ability of his own and perfect integrity in the use of it. He had listened to me with more attention than my rather incoherent outburst deserved. It was not only good manners, but real kindliness and a desire to enlighten that prompted him to take seriously what many others would have regarded as the callow uncertainties and the undigested rudiments of a still imperfect education.

'My dear young friend,' he said, 'you must certainly not think that you have offended us by being outspoken. What you have said makes me look even more favourably on you now than I did before, when you delighted Symmachus and myself with that excellent recitation from Virgil. I myself have often had such thoughts as those which you have just expressed and I too realize that such misgivings require satisfaction. You will be, I think, grateful to an old man, rather than indignant with him, if he attempts to show you that some of your views are mistaken. Let me begin with the point which you first raised, the apparent impurities and obscenities which are associated with some acts of worship. Now here I think it is important that we should attempt to be modest and to realize the true facts of nature and of ourselves. You and I, of course, are philosophers and we know that behind all appearance, all contradiction, all corruption and dissolution there is a supreme power and goodness and wisdom. The spiritual philosopher may even imagine that by pure contemplation this supreme being is accessible to him. This, certainly, is what Plotinus thought; though it is interesting to observe that Plato, a greater mind than Plotinus, seems less certain of such purely intellectual apprehension. It remains true, however, that most men and women are not philosophers at all. Yet all men have, in different degrees, an aspiration towards the divine. I suggest that there are many different paths all leading in the direction of the same end. Some paths will take one further than others; none is without some value for some people. Think of the size of our empire, and of the variety of races, characters, intelligences and dispositions which it comprises. Should we cut ourselves off from humanity, we shall cease to be human ourselves. Think also of the long period of time past during which the needs of humanity have been felt, recognized, and, to some extent, met. It is only a madman who would wish to deny the past, since, if we sever our connection with it, we can have no present and no future.

'Should we not, then, be modest and recognize that in many religious rites which appear to a philosopher uncouth or obscene, there is still an element that can make for the salvation of others and of ourselves? One who is intellectually incapable of grasping the unity and purity of the supreme being may be able to grasp something, some element of solace and of truth, in circumstances which to us may seem repellent. In the nocturnal orgies of Bacchus, for instance, the power of divinity (both dangerous and beneficent) can be felt. Even in such ecstasies as result in voluntary castration, there is an aim towards a different incorporation, a pursuit of power beyond the world of sense—though we, with the responsibility of a great empire, do well, I think, to discourage these acts among Roman citizens. I think, my dear Alypius, that we shall do neither well nor wisely if we judge all others by precisely the same standards as we apply to ourselves. A philosopher or a scholar will not wish frequently to be disturbed by violent sexual excitement; he is perhaps seeking God in a different way. But an ordinary man or woman may find in the very emotions which the philosopher, for his own reasons, rejects the only path to some understanding of the mysteries which alone, when we have fulfilled our social duties, give meaning to our lives. We have a duty, to my mind, to tolerate every effort that man makes and has made to transcend his human limitations, so long as these efforts do not entail crime. You are right, of course, to condemn human sacrifices, though you could be wrong to dismiss from your mind the symbolic truth which some of these ceremonies have implied or foreshadowed.

'Let us, therefore, in the first place be tolerant. Then, it seems to me, we can advance further towards the object which we all seek to find. And here both my wife and I would speak to you from a living experience, not from hearsay nor from any contrivance of theoretical argument. As you know, my wife and I have been initiated in many mysteries. We have bathed in the blood of the Bull and of the Ram; we have been privileged, after long and arduous preparations, to share in the illuminations not only of Mithra, but of Isis and Osiris and the Ceres of Eleusis. Naturally we cannot speak to you of what has been revealed to us; but we can tell you, in all sincerity, that we know that we are happy in this world and in the next. Nor will you imagine, I am sure, that we are victims of credulity or superstition. And there are plenty of witnesses, apart from us, of the truth of what I am saying. No doubt you have read the works of your own African writer, Apuleius of Madaura. Is it not evident in his writing that by means of that power to which we give, among many other names, the name of Isis he was enabled to see and understand more of reality than was accessible to him as a philosopher?

'The chief faults which I have to find with the Christians are their intolerance and rigidity. I do not regard their mysteries as being absurd. That their Christ was born from a virgin seems to me credible. So was Apollonius of Tyana, who also is known to have performed more and greater miracles than Jesus. And one cannot deny that there are some extremely intelligent men among the Christians—Ambrose, for instance, the Bishop of Milan, is a fine scholar, an excellent administrator and a good man. I agree with you too about their useful and beneficent activities among the poor and the sick. This was an aspect of their religion which my friend the Emperor Julian wished to see incorporated into the worship of our own temples. But to maintain that this sect alone has the key to life and understanding seems to me both arrogant and ridiculous. The great universe of mind and of nature is too big for such simplifications. And I do not observe that the Christians are any different from people of other persuasions by any immunity from vice, vanity and ostentation. Here in Rome there are many of the young clergy who seem to spend their whole time in the pursuit of more or less pious ladies. Their love affairs are, to my mind, somewhat disgraceful, as is their shameless pursuit of legacies. For, as you will have noticed, they are by no means indifferent to money and to power. The present Bishop of Rome, Damasus, is quite a good scholar and, I think, reasonably honest; but he is richer than any of us. I offended him once by saying that if I could be Bishop of Rome, I might even be tempted to become a Christian. That was when I was prefect of this city and had the unpleasant task of putting down the disgraceful rioting of the Christians who fought in the streets for their rival candidates for this supreme post. They actually managed to kill three hundred of themselves before my troops could restore order. Yet they claim to have a religion of peace and are usually reluctant to engage in military service.'

Here Praetextatus broke off. He smiled first at his wife and then at me. 'My dear boy,' he said, 'you must forgive an old man for treating you rather as though you were in a lecture hall than at a dinner party. I can only say that I was interested in your own views and flattered myself that you might be interested in mine.'

I had indeed been interested, but I was still more confused. It seemed hard to deny the truth of everything that Praetextatus had said. Moreover he was trustworthy in himself. He was a man clearly incapable of deceit, fear, envy or any other of those moral weaknesses which, if present in the speaker, must detract from an argument however apparently logical. Yet still I felt that there was something wrong, something lacking in so much good sense, such evident integrity, such high principles. I wished that Augustine had been with me. He is as eloquent as Praetextatus himself and even though he is scarcely older than I am he is already known for his learning. Only last year he read and understood without any commentary or any professional instruction the *Categories* of Aristotle and explained his reading to us in the most lucid way, making what seemed so difficult perfectly easy. I remembered, however, that the translation of the *Categories* which Augustine had read had been made some years ago by

Praetextatus himself. On this instance, therefore, I could scarcely maintain that my friend is a better philosopher than the older man; and certainly he has had only a fraction of his experience. Yet still I felt that Augustine might have been able to express in words a meaning towards which I was only capable of groping. Something, it seemed to me, had been left unsaid or unnoticed. But I cannot say what this thing is and I cannot even see how there can be any other faculty required for the knowledge of truth except intelligence, scholarship, integrity and virtue.

So we talked for some time longer and I found myself listening with interest, excitement and affection to my hosts and still puzzled that, in spite of this, I could only assent reluctantly and, as it were, from impotence to their well-ordered arguments and their evident goodwill. Indeed, though philosophy and religion are the subjects which interest me more than all others, I was actually relieved when the conversation turned to my legal studies and to reminiscences of friends in Thagaste and at Carthage. It was with strangely mixed feelings that I went back late at night to my apartment with two of Praetextatus' slaves to escort me. I had been delighted and excited by the evening, by the beauty and goodness and ease of Paulina, by the charm, strength and intelligence of her husband. Yet I missed something, and perhaps it was the freshness and the possibly uncouth enthusiasm of the talks I had had with Augustine and Nebridius. Yet was not our very urgency a sign of uncertainty and of dissatisfaction? And can these be held to be either worthy or comfortable states of mind?

III

It has so happened that within a few days of my visit to Praetextatus I have met this celebrated monk Jerome, whom Paulina so much dislikes. My kinsman Romanianus had given me a number of commissions for friends of his. Among these friends is a lady, Marcellina by name, who has an estate in Africa though she spends most of her time in Rome with her husband. I had been asked to take her a silver ink-stand, a really fine piece of Moorish work, and I had also brought a few quails to bring her on my own account. When I reached her house, I was informed that she had gone out to visit some friends on the Aventine Hill and I was encouraged to go and find her there. As I had been instructed to give the ink-stand into her own hands, I overcame my natural reluctance to call on people whom I did not know, and I took the quails along with me, since I was afraid that the servants would either steal them or substitute inferior birds if I left them behind.

I am by nature somewhat shy in social life and I had taken trouble that day with my dress. I had some good leather shoes which did not show a single crease; my clothes were soft and light and I had had my hair curled early in the morning.

When I reached the house and had stated my business to the doorkeeper, there was a considerable delay before I was admitted. And even when I was finally allowed inside the door, I was left standing some time in the hall. Soon I began to fear that my visit was inconvenient and to wish that I had not come. Finally, however, I heard steps approaching and saw that a young woman had come out from one of the inner rooms and was advancing to greet me. Her hair, which was tinted gold, was elaborately dressed in a high knot on her head; she wore a lilac cloak and she walked almost as though she were dancing. She announced herself as Marcellina and welcomed me as though she had known me all her life. 'So you are Alypius,' she said. 'I've often heard of you from Romanianus. He told me you were handsome, and you certainly are.'

I was somewhat embarrassed as she looked over me as though I were some kind of racehorse which she was appraising; but her manner was cheerful and unaffected so that I soon felt at ease with her. When I gave her the presents her eyes showed her delight. She moved quickly towards me and kissed me lightly on the face. 'You are sweet,' she said. 'And quails too? How did you know I liked them? Now you must come in and let me show you to the others.'

I attempted to excuse myself, since I imagined that these ladies, if they had really wished to see me, would have invited me in themselves. But Marcellina was persistent. She took me by the arm and said, 'No, I won't let you go. You must come in, if only for my sake. By the way, are you a Christian?'

I said that my mother was and was about to declare that I myself was unbaptized, when Marcellina interrupted me. 'Then that's quite all right,' she said. 'As a matter of fact I am too. But I really couldn't be like the women here. Believe it or not, they spend nearly the whole day singing psalms.' She raised her eyebrows and continued: 'And in Hebrew too! Just imagine.'

'Well,' I said, 'they won't want to see me. It would be much better if I didn't disturb them.'

But Marcellina was determined. 'I don't suppose they will want to see you,' she said, 'but I do.' She laughed again. 'As a matter of fact they seem to think that there's something wrong in being a man. I can't tell you how bored I've been. They aren't very pleased to see me either, and they ought to be, as I'm a relation and anyway it's good for them to see someone sometimes instead of praying all the time. And several of them are just my own age. I can understand Blaesilla looking unhappy, as she's just lost her husband, but the others are making her more unhappy still. I'd really have left myself by now, if I hadn't sent my carriage and eunuchs away for half an hour. Come on, you must come in. You needn't talk to anyone except me. They probably won't want to talk to you anyway.'

Her remarks, friendly as they were, did not have the effect of putting me any more at my ease. But Marcellina was wholly indifferent to this. She laughed again and gave me another light kiss on the forehead. 'You really are sweet,' she said. I found myself liking her. Normally I would have been frightened, but there was nothing immodest in her kisses. Indeed she reminded me of Lucilla, Augustine's mistress, who is always kind to me and behaves towards me with the same affectionate playfulness. This is partly because I am Augustine's friend and partly because she likes me. Augustine is always amused when he sees us together.

So, being propelled forward by Marcellina, I found myself in a dimly lighted room where three ladies, all young, were sitting in silence. Each was reading in a book and each spoke the normal polite words of greeting when Marcellina introduced me. What surprised me, though, was that none of them raised her eyes to my face. Their manner was gentle, but they showed not the slightest wish to become further acquainted.

I have forgotten the names of two of these ladies. The name Blaesilla remained in my memory, partly because I had heard her spoken of before, partly because she particularly engaged my attention by the extreme pallor of her face and beauty of her expression. I think I have seen no one looking at the same time so beautiful and so ill.

Marcellina appeared perfectly indifferent to the general atmosphere of constraint. 'This is Alypius,' she was saying. 'He comes from Africa and is friend of a great friend of mine. He's brought me this lovely ink-stand and, since he's an absolutely charming boy, he brought me some lovely quails too.'

No one showed any interest in the ink-stand, the quails or

myself. Marcellina was looking vexed and I, partly in order to prevent her speaking, said to one of the ladies. 'May I inquire what you are reading?'

'I am reading,' she said, 'the prophet Obadiah.' Again she spoke with the utmost politeness, but avoided looking at me. I began to feel like a disincarnated voice, an invisible man. Moreover, I could think of nothing else to say. Though I am reasonably well acquainted with literature, I had never heard of this writer.

Even Marcellina appeared, for the moment, chilled by an atmosphere which, though in no way hostile, was most evidently icy. We might have been in the presence of mountains. I thought of a phrase from Virgil, but there did not seem to be any point in quoting it. Marcellina came close to me and clutched my arm. 'Tell them, Alypius my dear,' she said. 'They must at least look at my quails.' No one moved. Marcellina turned her face fully towards me. I could see that her teeth had been sharpened and whitened with pumice-stone and her eyes darkened with antimony. She had rather too much white lead on her face, but her expression was pathetic, like that of a child. 'I love quails,' she said.

At this moment another visitor arrived. He came into the room quickly and unannounced, but somehow he made his presence felt immediately. The three ladies rose to their feet, smiling, and I could now see that they possessed, with the utmost modesty, every grace which can be associated with women of the highest breeding. They began to speak with a freedom that almost amounted to animation. I recall such phrases as 'Welcome, in the name of Christ', 'We have been hoping that you might find time to come', and 'We trust that you are in no hurry.'

I was studying the man himself and finding him curiously impressive. He was about the middle height and his rough gown was, to say the least, shabby. He walked awkwardly with a somewhat limping step. Yet one was only dimly conscious of these characteristics. He seemed to generate some invisible force. something difficult to describe, forbidding, powerful, yet not wholly repulsive. His eyes had the same kind of fire that I have often noticed in Augustine's eyes when he is carried away by some strong feeling; but this fire was more concentrated and somehow less human. For Augustine is not only forceful and brilliant but gentle, affectionate and extraordinarily charming. This man had nothing about him that could deserve any of these adjectives as they are commonly used; and yet I could feel a different and a most powerful fascination in his hard eyes. They were not only vehement and intolerant and arrogant, but seemed full of sadness. For no reason that I could name I felt a kind of sympathy towards him, although he made it quite evident by his expression that he resented my presence even more than that of Marcellina. He glanced with particular distaste at my hair and at my new shoes.

'This is our cousin, Marcellina,' said one of the ladies, 'and this is a friend of hers from Africa, Alypius of Thagaste.' She then introduced the newcomer to us as 'our friend and father, the holy Jerome'.

By this time Marcellina had recovered her self-confidence. 'Oh,' she said eagerly, 'I've heard such a lot about you. How fascinating! You are the man who thinks that we all ought to be virgins.'

Jerome had been looking at me with a kind of hostility which, to my knowledge, I had done nothing to deserve. He now turned to Marcellina. He spoke surprisingly gently.

'Since the earliest times,' he said, 'the Church has commended virginity.'

He was about to say more and I observed that the other three ladies were gazing with a rapt attention at his face. But Marcellina broke in. 'Oh no,' she said, 'you really are wrong there. Only the other day I heard that it has been changed. There is a very holy man and a great scholar (I've forgotten his name, but it doesn't matter) who says that we are all the same—wives, widows, virgins—in Christ, as long, of course, as we do our duty. He says too that it's quite all right to marry again if one's husband dies. The only thing that's wrong is adultery, but I suppose you can repent of that too.'

The expression of Jerome's face had changed alarmingly during this speech. His thin lips tightened, his eyes blazed with a kind of contempt that seemed to scorch the very furniture in the room. Even Marcellina appeared frightened, though I could see that this fierce and trenchant emotion of his was directed not at her but at the views she had been advancing.

'You should acquire,' he said, 'some rudimentary acquaintance with the facts before you indulge yourself in theorizing. The ignorant fool whom you are commending and who has seduced the little good sense that you possess is an obscene monster of the name of Jovinianus. To call such a third-rate rhetorician a scholar is to deprive language of all meaning. To call him "good" is to deny the existence of virtue. He is a bombastic ass without the slightest ability to put down in order two consecutive ideas. His filthy and distorted mind (if it can be called one) merely spews out nauseating trash.'

Marcellina, at first taken aback by the violence of the language and by the rasping tones in which it was spoken, quickly regained her confidence. 'Yes,' she said, 'Jovinianus. That's the name. But he says that you are wicked and stupid too. Of course I'm sure he's wrong. All the same I still can't make out why you condemn marriage. Didn't God say 'Increase and Multiply'? And didn't Jesus go to the marriage in Cana? And, in any case, isn't it perfectly natural? I mean, how would there be any children otherwise?'

I saw the veins standing out on Jerome's forehead and noticed his jaw tighten. Again, however, his rage was not against Marcellina. If he looked at her with contempt, there was in the contempt a certain pity, even a certain affection. 'I beg you,' he said, 'in the first place to stick to facts, and secondly to try to impart some rational meaning to your words. Finally I do not condemn marriage and never have done. To say that I condemn marriage is a lying and calumnious invention characteristic of that illiterate mountebank (who, incidentally, is also as ugly as an ape) whom you, in your weakness and folly, think that you admire. You may (since you are evidently uneducated) admire his style too; you cannot admire his arguments, since they do not exist, or his authority, since he has none.'

Marcellina now showed a disposition to break off the discussion. 'Oh well,' she said, 'I'm very glad anyway that you do approve of marriage. You see I somehow got the impression that you thought we all ought to be virgins. Now I understand.'

'It is perfectly evident,' said Jerome, 'that you understand nothing. I do not condemn a lunatic or a leper. That does not mean that I approve of lunacy or leprosy. Gold, silver and copper are all of value, but not all of equal value. Between approving a great good and condemning something evidently bad there must be many gradations. And on marriage the teaching of the Church and of the Apostle is perfectly plain. Marriage may be a necessity and within the married state a certain degree of goodness and piety is certainly possible. But such a state must, in the nature of things, be less perfect than the state of virginity. That is simply a fact. Virginity once lost can never be recovered. Only the second best is possible. And the second best is for those who have become married to agree by mutual consent to live together in chastity. The third best is to satisfy within the bonds of wedlock those inordinate lusts which might otherwise run riot in indiscriminate fornication, to beget and to bear children and to seek by prayer a greater measure of self-control. If I approve of marriage, it is because marriage gives me virgins. A widow or a widower can never regain the virginity that has been lost, but they are at least free from the obligations of a wife to her husband and of a husband to his wife.'

28

'All the same,' said Marcellina, 'I don't see why one shouldn't marry again. Not if it isn't wrong. Why shouldn't Blaesilla marry again, for instance? Her family has a long line of consuls. Has she not a duty to her family? I mean, apart from the fact that she might fall in love.'

I was surprised that Jerome now spoke with an extraordinary gentleness. His eyes rested briefly on the beautiful pale face of Blaesilla, as she sat still reading her book. 'Blaesilla,' he said, 'has chosen a marriage more glorious than any that can be shown in the records of the Scipios or the Camilli. Her service is to the living God.' I saw that the whole expression of his face had changed. The harshness and the violence had gone and been replaced by a tenderness and a kind of reverence, indeed a delicacy that was wholly unexpected. For a moment he seemed lost in a happy contemplation. Then he remembered Marcellina and again his expression changed. 'You,' he said, 'might grow more like her and might reap a richer reward than anything that is available to you now. But first you would have to see yourself as you are. You would have to realize how ludicrous you look with your waving hairdress and your unnaturally painted face. How wantonly and how shamelessly you walk with your tripping, mincing steps, how everything about you is designed to arouse the filthiest and most boiling lust. Thou hast a whore's forehead; thou refusest to be ashamed.'

Marcellina was, I could see, both shocked and offended by this speech. In a somewhat childish gesture, she stamped one foot on the ground and bit her lip. But before she could speak, Jerome began again. He had now noticed the quails and was pointing at them with disgust. 'You would have to learn,' he said, 'that there is death in the pot. You cram your belly with quails. The result is undigested food and hiccoughs which inflame passion. Your stuffed and surfeited stomach will communicate its heat to the other members. You will even, perhaps, use the word "love" to describe a beastly wallowing in stinking sweat. The devil's strength is in the loins and navel. I admonish you now as a father. Give heed to my words before your skirt is above your head and your nakedness discovered.'

Marcellina's face was pale with anger and there were tears of anger in her eyes. Jerome appeared quite indifferent to the impression which his words had made. He turned quickly to the three ladies, excluding Marcellina, myself and the quails from his attention. 'Come,' he said, 'I have only an hour to spare. We will sing a psalm and then see what progress you have made with your Hebrew.'

Marcellina appeared for a moment to be about to speak, but evidently could find no words. She tossed her head back and walked directly from the room. I bowed to the eldest one of the three ladies and then hurried after her. When I reached the door, I remembered the quails, but felt somehow reluctant to go back for them. To my surprise Jerome spoke to me in a voice which was, if not exactly kindly, at least polite. 'You have forgotten your birds, young man,' he said, and, as I stopped to pick them up, he added: 'In spite of the vulgar display evident in your clothes and hair, you appear to me to have a certain innocence. Try to preserve it.'

I was looking at the quails and the sight of them made me somehow sad. Blood was trickling from their beaks and there were milky films over their eyes; the beautiful feathers had lost lustre; the heads flopped and rolled on flaccid necks which, when they were alive, had had the quick muscular grace of serpents. I remembered the quails hunts we had had in the hills near Thagaste and how when the birds were in the nets they had often seemed to me too beautiful to kill. Yet I had killed them, partly from pride in my own dexterity as a hunter, partly because, in some part of me, I enjoyed it.

Jerome was speaking again and his voice, though solemn, was again gentle. He seemed to be talking as it were indifferently to himself, to me and to the ladies. 'Often,' he said, 'I have seen these birds in the desert and have blessed them. They are incapable either of virtue or of sin, but they, like all creation, glorify God and indicate His splendour. While I lay on the ground groaning, my skin burned black by the sun, my body wasted by fasting, my soul torn by evil desires and wicked imaginations, these birds would flutter over my foul body and my fouler soul, a flock and swarm of praise to Him who made all things good, and a reminder to us of our fallen state. None of us, no man and no woman, can rival them in beauty, yet even their beauty vanishes in death. They rot on earth and pullulate with worms, if they are not turned to excrement from the bodies of men. Our bodies are like theirs, only less beautiful and less innocent. They are not even aware of their inevitable corruption. But we know, and how often do we deliberately prefer death to life, filthiness to purity? Oh God, be merciful to me, a sinner!'

I was now as much attracted to the man by his fervour and sincerity and also by the almost desperate sadness in his voice as previously I had been repelled by the coarseness of his language and what had seemed to me his quite unjustifiable rudeness to Marcellina. Again, as so often, I found my mind torn in different directions. It seemed to me that Praetextatus, with his perfect manners, would have been incapable of deliberately wounding the feelings of another; but he would have been equally incapable of taking seriously this final expression of a genuine humility which had followed so quickly upon what had appeared to be an arrogance of moral and intellectual pride.

Still confused, I went quickly from the room. Marcellina, with her servants and her eunuchs about her, had already left. It seemed to me that I should be acting with most delicacy if I forbore from following her. So I took the quails back to my landlord.

IV

How bitterly I re-read the words that I have written so far! For now, within so few weeks of my coming to Rome, I am fallen back entirely even from that wretched state which I had been in. When I spoke to Praetextatus and to Jerome, I was at least able to appreciate the integrity of these men and recognized the fact that each of them, though in ways that I could scarcely understand, was seeking for the truth I sought and had, in different ways, reached the answer that I so much desired. But now I am not fit for their company. I have deserted my own resolution, broken the promises I made both to my mother and to Augustine. And it is worse than this, because I know that I shall go again to the games tomorrow.

I still cannot understand how it happened. I had been, as usual, to my classes in the morning with the other law students, all of whom are my friends, though they laugh at me when I refuse to accompany them on their evening expeditions after girls. As we were walking back from the lecture room Valerianus said to us all, 'Let's go to the amphitheatre. We'll just have time, and there's a marvellous show of sword-fighters today.' The others were as enthusiastic as might be expected and then someone asked me to go with them. I said that I had some work to do and in any case wasn't fond of this spectacle. 'Oh, come,' said Valerianus, 'that's nonsense. We all remember you at Carthage. You never used to miss a day. It will do you good, Alypius. And we'll have a party afterwards.' They all began to urge me to come with them, but I was determined not to agree. Everyone was very merry and laughing and someone said, 'We're not going to let you off, Alypius. We'll drag you along with us for your own good.'

I was still laughing when I said, 'You can compel my body, if you like, but not my mind. If you force me into that place, I shall simply sit with my eyes shut until it's all over.' I meant precisely what I said, for I had lost all desire for the cruel sport and I remembered clearly the time when, accidentally (as he said afterwards), Augustine had saved me from my idle, inconsiderate vice. If I had not been so sure of myself, I should have resisted more. As it was I allowed myself to be dragged along and was amused as my friends made bets among each other as to whether I would or would not behave as I had promised to do.

The amphitheatre was already in an uproar by the time we entered. I had to keep my eyes open while we made our way to our seats, but I scarcely glanced at the arena. I was already disgusted by the smell of blood seeping up through the hot air. I noticed a few bodies—a giraffe, I think, and some bears —which were being dragged out, and I received a vague impression of bright clothes, sweating faces and a kind of general mad agitation which I found most repellent. How little did I realize that I should be part of the mass which I despised, as mad as anyone and more guilty than anyone since I had come there knowing and detesting the very madness which was to overwhelm me!

I was sitting between two of my friends and keeping my eyes tightly shut. As I listened to their conversation I was actually admiring my own self-control. It seemed so easy to refrain from this pleasure that I had once known in Carthage and of which I now thought so little. My friends were congratulating themselves on having arrived just in time for the gladiators; they were not at this stage paying much attention to me; I gathered from their conversation that there was a party of women or girls sitting not far away and that they were trying to get into conversation with them. Soon there was a great roar of voices from the whole audience. The shout in itself seemed to me bestial and equally bestial were the smells of the amphitheatre. One might have been oneself in a cage of beasts. With my eyes shut my other senses were more than ordinarily acute and most of the impressions they received were disgusting. I assumed that this burst of shouting indicated the arrival of the gladiators in the arena and I prepared, with a kind of pride, to cut myself off for some hours from the squalor of my surroundings. It seemed to me that I was superior to the rest.

And so for some time I listened to cheer and counter-cheer, to the frenzied yells of women, to brutal savage injunctions, to howls of delight provoked by the slaughter or mutilation of men. Then suddenly there was a moment of complete silence. No doubt the crowd were hushed in suspense as two particularly well-known champions were manœuvring for position. I do not know how long this silence lasted, but it was terminated as suddenly as it had begun by an explosion of sound far greater than anything I had heard before. Everyone, at one and the same moment, raised his voice in a kind of delighted and astonished uproar. It was like a thunderclap and it was just the suddenness of it, I suppose, that caused me to open my eyes.

I saw the two duellists standing just underneath me in the arena. The elder and shorter of the two had leapt inside the guard of his opponent, a tall fair-haired youth, probably a German. Somehow I realized, as though my eyes had been open all the time, exactly what had happened, and could estimate that precise perfection of skill shown by the shorter man which had roused the admiration of the crowd. He had achieved something technically decisive, something perfectly brilliant. One could see it in the eyes of the German youth, who for a moment turned his head aside, knowing that nothing could save him. All this I saw and realized in an infinitesimal moment of time, for even as my eyes opened the victor had passed to the final moment and had buried his sword up to the hilt in the young man's neck. Then, with a quick twist of the arm, he withdrew the weapon and stepped back a pace. The yellow-haired youth who had been his opponent fell sideways and slumped upon the sand. For a moment his limbs twitched and then he lay still.

And now I found myself on my feet. I was shouting with the rest. I watched the blood flow and cried out for more. I followed every subsequent fight as though my own life depended on it and indeed it almost seemed to me as though it was I myself who was thrusting and parrying, wounding and being wounded, so fully was I identified with the whole act and elaboration of savagery. Now the smell of blood seemed natural and good; the skill shown in butchery seemed the best and noblest of skills. I could have watched the spectacle for hour after hour and, when it was over, I could talk of nothing else for the rest of the evening. Later my friends began by laughing at me for the total change in the complexion of my taste and resolution, but I was quite indifferent to their remarks and soon they too came under the sway of my enthusiasm as we went over every detail of the fight, commenting on feats of skill or exhibitions of cowardice, rousing up again in ourselves the excitement which we had shared.

Not until that night, when I was alone in my apartment, did I become conscious of the ignominy of my conduct and the extent of my weakness. And then these thoughts came to me, as it were, accidentally. It happened that my eyes fell on a copy of Virgil's *Eclogues* which had been given me by Augustine as a parting present before I left Africa. He had had no design in giving me this particular book; he knew simply how fully I shared his own enthusiasm for Virgil; yet it almost seemed to me now that it could not have been by chance that this book and no other had been his choice; for it, of all books, reminded me of another scene, another accident (as he has often told me), but an accident which I had believed had altered my life. How ashamed I feel now that I find that my life has not been altered! Because I know that next time there is a show on in the amphitheatre, so far from resisting the invitations of my friends, I shall be the first to suggest going and I shall drag them along with me. I know clearly that this savage pleasure is a degradation of character and a waste of time; but equally clearly I know that I shall pursue it. Can it be that there is no logic at all in the nature of man? Are will and resolution mere subjective illusions, some function of atomic movement or of different spiritual powers which in momentary and shifting ways possess us? It cannot be so. Augustine, I know, would never be subject to my weakness. And yet he too, as he has often pointed out to me, has a weakness of his own. Often he has congratulated me on my chastity and deplored the fact that he himself cannot go through a day without sexual activity. Yet, though I personally find this activity disgusting, I must allow it to be human. And if Augustine does regard himself as being too uncontrollably under the influence of sexual desire, at least that desire seems to be a genuine part of our nature and has been either tolerated or commended by many good men. How different from my vice, which demands for its satisfaction the death of others and the brutalization of myself.

And how humiliating it is to find that I have fallen again into a vice from which I had imagined myself entirely to have escaped! It was Augustine who freed me from it (or so I thought) about eighteen months ago when I was attending his lectures in Carthage. It was during the time (only, I am glad to say, a short time) when we had been somewhat estranged from each other, and how happily this estrangement ended!

Of course I have known Augustine since childhood. We both came from Thagaste. He is a little older than I am and first memories of him are simply ones of admiration for his superior strength and intellectual abilities. It was not till I was about fourteen that we became close friends, and of this friendship my mother has always approved, partly, I think, because of her admiration for Augustine's mother, Monnica; but there was a time when my father did everything in his power to prevent any intimacy between us. He would offend my mother by mocking at what he described as the ridiculously exaggerated and uncouth piety of Monnica and he had never held a high opinion of Augustine's father, Patricius, who, according to him, would have been richer than he was if he had given more attention to his farm and been less inclined to quarrel with his neighbours. But it was Augustine himself of whom, at that time, my father chiefly disapproved. He certainly recognized, as everyone else in our town did, the great promise of the boy, but, unlike my relative Romanianus, he had refused to do anything to help him to continue his education after he had finished school at Madaura, where he had won every kind of honour. So Augustine had to spend a year at home before he could go on to Carthage, helped by the generosity of Romanianus who was so impressed with the boy's abilities that he went about prophesying that in the future Thagaste would be as famous because of Augustine as Madaura was because of Apuleius. My father, however, while admitting the possibility that Augustine might have a great future, still regarded him as an unsuitable companion for me. He would call him 'wild', 'over-emotional', 'arrogant', 'irresponsible', but I think that he only used these adjectives to disguise from himself what was really a feeling of jealousy. After all these adjectives can be applied to most boys of spirit. Augustine was no wilder than the rest of us and was more responsible than any of us. He was and is intensely emotional and I have been told that, when a small boy, he would go to any lengths in order to win a game or a wrestling match, to help a friend or to injure an enemy. But by the time I came to know him he had outgrown all savagery and vulgarity in behaviour. His affection is extraordinarily intense, but also extraordinarily gentle. Where he loves there is no sign either of meanness or of arrogance. I fancy that what was chiefly resented was that I myself so readily followed Augustine's lead, that I was always quoting his opinions and that I was often tactless enough to compare them favourably with my father's own. So it seems to me that the quarrel which took place between my father and my friend was really of my making. With a little more tact it could have been prevented. As it was there was an occasion when my father became so exasperated at finding me continually taking Augustine's side in argument against him that he entirely lost his temper and let loose a flood of foolish and insulting invective against him. Augustine's usual manner in social intercourse is friendly and, without being subservient, appealing. His impulse is to like others and he expects to be liked himself. Yet this natural sweetness and softness of disposition can change in an instant into something cold, hard and forbidding if he feels himself insulted. He is very slow to take offence and indeed I have often known him to pass over without noticing it some unkind or rude remark addressed to him. For at this time of my father's outburst, he seemed for a moment to think that the words he heard spoken could neither be intended seriously nor understood according to their meanings. When he did grasp the obvious fact that my father was insulting him, he behaved in a manner that surprised me. I have known his face to go white with anger, his facial muscles to stiffen and his eyes to appear hard as ice. At such moments there is something terrible about him and afterwards he himself, even if he has had every excuse for anger, regrets the violence of an emotion quite disproportionate to its cause. But on this occasion he behaved differently. He was blushing and there were tears in his eyes; it was as though he, and not my father, were at fault. Without saying a word, he rose and left the house. When he had gone, my father turned to me and, in a kind of inane triumph, said 'You see that your friend is not only a conceited ass of an intellectual, but also a miserable coward.'

I myself was too ashamed and distressed to speak or act as I should have done. I threw myself down on a couch and burst into tears. Between my sobs I kept shouting out, 'It's not true! It's not true!' But I was incapable of saying anything more coherent than this and was indeed in such a state of hysterical misery that even my father became alarmed and began to speak kindly to me, attempting to persuade me that everything that he had said had been said for my good. I scarcely listened to him. I knew how bitterly my friend had been wounded and I knew that the forbearance and embarrassment which he had shown had been marks of his affection for me. Of course I should have run after him to console him and to explain to him, if it were necessary, my love and sympathy. But I was too upset by the whole incident and selfishly decided to put off all explanations till the next day. But next day was too late. Augustine had left immediately for Carthage. Soon afterwards I received a note from him. 'I am sorry', he wrote, 'that your father has taken such a dislike to me. This, of course, will make it impossible for you to become my pupil in Carthage. However, there are plenty of teachers in Carthage and perhaps some time we shall meet again.'

How often, since then, have we discussed this note, sometimes laughing over it and sometimes weeping. For it seems that, when deep feelings are involved, written words can be most cruel and most misleading. I myself regarded this note as a cold dismissal of my friendship. It seemed to me that Augustine was fully justified in this, yet that fact did not make me the less miserable. Augustine on his side had written, also in great distress, with the sole object of making it easy for me, if I wished, to obey my father, though he had hoped and believed that I would not do so. But I, having misunderstood his motives in writing, was too ashamed to reply; and he, from my silence, concluded that my affection for him was too weak to stand up to a parental prohibition. So, when I went to Carthage later in the year, I attended the classes of another teacher of rhetoric, thinking that Augustine would not welcome me at his class; and Augustine made no effort to get in contact with me, thinking that I was studiously avoiding him.

At this time he was the youngest teacher of rhetoric in Carthage and indeed had only just completed his own studies there. He had often told me about the student life in the city, the attractions of the theatres (to which he was very much addicted) and of the games, for which he had never had any taste. I myself, of course, had visited Carthage before, but I had never before lived there continuously. Now I found myself every day exposed to new impressions and these impressions were exciting enough in themselves to occupy a great portion of my thought and energy; though from time to time I would feel a weight upon my heart as I remembered how I had hoped and how I had promised myself that I should be sharing all these new experiences with my friend. However, I had other friends (though none so dear to me) and there were countless things in the city to be seen and admired.

My greatest passion was for the circus and for the gladiatorial shows and I wasted day after day in these empty and cruel amusements. My teacher of rhetoric attempted to reform me. He told me that he had regarded me as his most promising pupil, but that now I was falling behind the others. I could see that he was talking sense, but not only was I incapable of resisting my desires for blood, excitement and a display of skill—I actually took a kind of pleasure in deliberately doing what I knew was both foolish and wrong. And in some strange way the very thought of Augustine played a part in this perversion of mine. Somehow, since I could not see him, I found a delight in doing things of which I knew he would not approve.

One day I met him in the street. We were both embarrassed, but I greeted him and he, with his usual courtesy, returned my greeting. This happened several times and it pleased me even to have this remote kind of conventional contact with him, though I thought bitterly of how we had planned to spend all our spare time together when I was in Carthage. I knew the place where he held his classes and indeed I was acquainted with several of his pupils. These were among the richest, though not the most studious, of the youth of Africa. Many of them came from the rich quarter of the Hill and I, since my father had given me a handsome allowance, had begun to imitate their extravagant habits in dress. It was fashionable then to dye one's hair the colour of flame, to wear green or gold necklaces and to take infinite trouble in the choice of ear-rings. In Rome the same fashions were coming in; but they originated in Carthage and I, as a young and vain student from the country, was quick to follow them. Certainly I preferred the manner and conversation of these rather exquisite young men to the rough and boorish behaviour of that other group of students who became known as 'the trippers', since they delighted in every sort of horse-play, physical and intellectual. They took pride in insulting their professors, in disrupting the organization of the city, in brawling and in those kinds of practical jokes which are most savage, outrageous and cruel. Not many of these 'trippers' were students of Augustine; perhaps because his teaching was on an advanced level, perhaps because they preferred to persecute older men. But even among the other and more serious students there was little of the discipline which was found in Rome. It is quite normal in Carthage, for instance, to drop into a professor's class for ten minutes or so and then to go on to another. Neither the professor nor the students are surprised by this habit, which would certainly be regarded as discourteous in Rome. And so I, accompanied by friends who were his pupils, would sometimes attend Augustine's classes for short periods. I would sit quietly at the back and, after saluting him, would make my way out before the class was over.

One day I was there and did not think at first that he had noticed my presence. He was expounding a passage from Virgil and, in order to illustrate some point or other, had begun to give an exceedingly amusing account of the characters and disabilities of those who waste their time and money on the games and circuses. Many of his pupils, of course, could recognize themselves in his description, but his words, so beautifully arranged and diversified with wit, charm and severity, while certainly effective, displeased nobody. But on me they fell with a peculiar force. I remembered our long friendship and I was convinced that, though he had appeared not to notice me, he was in fact speaking to me personally. I saw, with some of his own precision and even with some of his own amusement, the stupidity and futility of my conduct. I blushed and trembled and kept my eyes fixed on the ground; and when I left as usual before the end of the class, I forgot even to bow to him on my way out.

Later that day I went to find him at his house and thanked him for his words and for his consideration for me. I had scarcely spoken a sentence when the first severity of his expression altered to the warmest smile. We were soon in each other's arms, each weeping on the other's shoulders. Everything was soon explained and our friendship was renewed. Indeed it had become the stronger because of the misunderstanding. Yet the reconciliation itself had been as accidental as had been the original breach. Augustine had not in fact noticed me in his audience until I had been on the point of leaving. His remarks had been in no way addressed to me, though he had heard that I was in fact ruining my abilities and wasting my time. He himself had been distressed at the thought that I might have imagined that he was deliberately insulting me.

How happy we were that evening! All the happier because of the bitterness of our separation. And we were sobered, too, by the though that it had been only because of an accident that our real feelings had been able to show themselves. Lucilla, who was with us for most of the time when she was not attending to the baby, insisted that it was no accident, but the work of God. She still retains more of the Christian belief in miracles than do Augustine and I. Yet even we, in our joy, were almost prepared to believe her in the miraculous. And from that moment until I came to Rome, we have been seeing each other every day. Even my father came to admit that he had been wrong and though at first it was only grudgingly that he gave me his permission to become a regular pupil of Augustine, he ended, since I won a certain amount of distinction, by believing that the idea had been his own.

And now, with all this love in my heart and all this certainty in my mind, I am doing deliberately what neither love nor intellect can commend. I know that I shall go to the games again tomorrow. That is certain. But cannot I think back again to the time when I knew peace?

V

Certainly I have known peace, but have I ever known it for more than an hour or a day at a time? I like to think that my early childhood was peaceful and contented, yet I know how we are tricked by our memory or lack of it. As the old poets did for the past we like to imagine a golden age in our own lives and we conveniently forget facts that will not fit in with this agreeable theory. I have seen this in the case of others, who have quite sincerely described to me their great happiness on certain occasions and at certain ages. But often I have remembered these very occasions myself and have been able accurately to recall the extreme misery, awkwardness or humiliation of the very people who later claimed to have been just then so happy. And I myself tend to create a mythical childhood in my own memory. It is based on the facts that my parents were comfortably off and were kind to me, that I was never subject, as other boys often are, to deliberate cruelty and never hungry. And with these facts in mind I tend to forget all the real terror, disappointments, agitations and perplexities which are incidental to childhood and which may well impress themselves all the more firmly on our characters the more we thrust them from our consciousness.

In particular people are apt to speak with hypocrisy about their school-days. They remember the distinctions they won or the friends they made and forget altogether how they shook with terror at the master's rod, how they were humiliated by their own ignorance or incapacity or by the cruelty or insensitivity of others; how, when they intended courage, they revealed themselves as cowards; how they pretended generosity, when all the time their hearts were filled with envy, malice or jealousy; how they took mean advantage of others and assumed this to be justice; how their hatred was savage and their love self-protective and self-centred. True that the impetus towards courage and generosity and wisdom is real; usually, too, we admit that these qualities are not easily acquired; but what we forget are the actual occasions when we have ourselves been cowardly, mean and deliberately perverse or stupid.

Of all my friends I think that Augustine has the clearest and most accurate ideas of his childhood. He is more passionate, more vigorous and more intellectually subtle than I am, and, while I tend to contemplate life with a growing perplexity, he is determined to find a meaning and to achieve an aim. He examines and sets in order his own thought and his own memory with the same skill and objectivity which he shows in literary criticism and composition. I shared much of my childhood with him and we have often discussed together the events and feelings of that time.

It seems to me that I have always known Augustine. In fact, however, I can remember very little about him in the early days when we were at school together in Thagaste. Of course he was a few years older than I and he tells me that he can remember me well in the time before he left Thagaste and went on to the more advanced school in Madaura. I was a popular boy, he says, and he attributes this partly to my natural docility and partly to what he calls my good nature. Certainly I seem to have kept out of serious trouble, but this may simply have been because of my lack of ambition. I have never been eager to occupy the first place in anything and have often been blamed for this by my relations. However, I do not appear to have quarrelled or fought with the other boys and, since I found the lessons easy, I did not resent the time spent on them and, being uncritical of the methods, did not fall foul of the schoolmaster. Here I differed from Augustine. He has always had a more independent character than mine and he had told me how he used to grit his teeth with rage when he was compelled in class to repeat for the thousandth time some sentence or mathematical table which he knew perfectly well already. He loved to play and he was always ambitious to be first in any game or trial of strength. He was passionately fond of his friends and would, at this time, tend to devote himself exclusively to one or two boys whom he would expect to feel the same exclusive affection for him. If they did not do so, he felt not only aggrieved, but personally guilty. It seemed to him natural that he should be loved, and, when the love he found was less than that which he gave, he considered that he must have committed some fault.

He, far more than I, suffered from the beatings which it is customary to inflict on children at school. It was not the pain that he minded (indeed he can bear pain better than anyone I know); what he resented was a kind of humiliation. In particular, as he has often told me, he was horrified and shocked by the attitude taken up by his parents on this subject. That they could actually laugh and make jokes about his sufferings seemed to him incredible, and he was most of all wounded by the fact that here his mother seemed to take sides with his father against him. For Augustine was inclined (somewhat unjustly, I think) to despise his father, while he loved (and still loves) his mother with great devotion. And indeed Monnica deserves his devotion, even though, to my mind, she seems to cling to her son with an excessive intensity. She would have him think exactly as she does, and I have known her to weep for hours on end when she has heard him express some view that is in opposition to the Christian faith. She resents the presence of his mistress and his child and indeed there was a time when she refused to sit at the same table with them. Then she explained her attitude by saying that she was shocked at his becoming a Manichee; but I am inclined to think that her real motive was the jealousy she felt at seeing him happy with another woman. It seems to me that her affection for Augustine has intensified since the death of her husband Patricius. In the days when he was still alive and when we were still at school, she gave most of her attention to him and though she seemed to prefer Augustine to either his brother or his sister, she was by no means exclusively attached to him. I, and I think most of the schoolchildren of Thagaste, remember her for her kindness and the sweetness of her disposition. We never laughed at her remarkable display of piety. For she would constantly be seen with a small basket of dainties and a small jug of wine mixed with water, bustling on her way to and from the chapels of saints and martyrs where she would enjoy some decorous feasting with her friends. In these matters she was always respectable, though other Christians often make these religious ceremonies occasions for drunken orgies and, when the chapels are in secluded places, for adulterous assignations. Monnica, however, so I have been told, would immediately leave one of these gatherings at the first appearance of any coarse language or impropriety; even her husband, Patricius, apt as he was to scoff at Christians in general, respected his wife's faith and indeed became a Christian himself before he died. He was a rough man, hot-tempered, but not at all ill-natured. He would make much of having his own way and being, as he put it, 'master in his own house'; sometimes he would be severe; but what he chiefly liked was a kind of rude jollity and he used to be both surprised and vexed when he found that neither his wife nor his favourite son responded to his jests. Monnica was offended by their coarseness, Augustine by their simplicity and lack of taste. For Augustine was undoubtedly Patricius' favourite, though he was less like his father than either of the other two children and indeed must often have been quite incomprehensible to him. In this lack of understanding I found something pathetic. For Patricius, without being able to estimate his son's abilities himself, would listen eagerly to, and would afterwards repeat, all the praise of these which he heard from others. It is doubtful whether he had any real respect for learning, but he was well aware that in our days a first-class professor of literature and rhetoric could reach the highest positions in the empire. Such a position he wanted for his son, partly because he was a poor man who had had to struggle all his life to meet the demands of tax-collectors and of a growing family; but partly also because of a genuine affection for Augustine, an affection which he could only express by planning for him a future into which he could not possibly enter himself. For long before we left school our normal conversation would be on subjects of which Patricius was wholly ignorant. He would, I remember, listen with a rather stupidly proprietary air, as of one who is contemplating a performing dog of his own, when we discussed music or poetry. Augustine was irritated by this attitude, though I found it, in an odd way, appealing. Indeed Augustine was annoyed by almost every display of interest in him which his father might take. Once, for instance, at the baths Patricius happened for the first time to observe that his son was no longer a sexless child, but was growing up into manhood. This was something which he could understand and, roaring with laughter, he pointed at the boy's nakedness and then, with the best of intentions, began to comment on some of the uses to which the sexual organ could be put and to describe what his own joy would be when he became a grandfather. I was present at the time and, though it occurred to me that my own father would never have spoken so coarsely or with such lack of taste, I was impressed by the real affection behind Patricius' ill-chosen words. Augustine, however, was deeply shocked. He was not a virgin even at this age; in fact he had already begun to suggest that I should

47

join him on some of his visits to the brothels in Madaura, a thing which I did not do until later, and then only once. Certainly when he was talking with us boys he would give us the impression that he was well acquainted with all aspects of love and, in a rather dim way, we used to admire him for it. But now, when his father was attempting, however crudely, to talk to him as man to man, his attitude surprised us. He blushed, he trembled, and then, bursting into a flood of tears, ran to collect his clothes and to leave the baths. Patricius was as annoyed and downcast as we were. He even turned to us as though for assurance. 'What did I say,' he asked us, 'to upset him? After all, I was a boy myself once.' Though we knew this to be a historical fact, it still seemed to us, as we looked at his rough face and his eyes bulging in an indecorous dismay, almost incredible. Most of us turned away from him coldly and contemptuously. We were offended that our leader had been put out of countenance. One boy said insolently, 'I expect your son could teach you more than you ever knew', and Patricius, grabbing him by the arm, began to beat him about the head. The action only momentarily relieved his feelings. Soon he let the boy go and we watched him walk slowly from the baths with a puzzled expression on his face.

I mention this trifling incident of childhood which Augustine and I have often discussed together because it seems to me an example of that strange turmoil of uncertainty and of a kind of terror in which, however much we like to idealise the period, much of our childhood is in fact spent. There was nothing in the words of Patricius calculated to excite that frenzy of shame and bitterness from which Augustine immediately suffered; nor had he any wish to wound his father, whose manner, though crude, had been intended to be friendly and even affectionate. No injury had been meant, yet each had been injured. Augustine himself was quick to recognize the differences and also the similarities between his feelings on this occasion and the rage that he used to feel when his parents questioned him laughingly about his beatings at

48

school. The beatings were, in a sense, a humiliation (and he feels all humiliation more keenly than others) and he seemed to have a right to feel affronted when those most dear to him, who should be the first to protect him, made light of what he considered an affliction. But there had been nothing derogatory about the remarks of Patricius in the baths. It would have seemed natural merely to have laughed at them and, even if one had been offended by one's father's lack of breeding, at least to have given him credit for his kindly intentions. Yet Augustine had found these words humiliating also. Here, too, in some way his self-esteem had been wounded, though for this wound there seemed to be no logical reason; he was more inclined to be proud than ashamed of his growing sexuality. Or was he perhaps, secretly and almost unbeknownst to himself, in fact ashamed of it? Here I must own myself to be at a loss, for, though I know that in most respects all children will react in much the same ways to the same events or situations, there are certainly cases where such a rule does not apply. There are, it seems to me, even in our childhood, depths of which we know nothing, real impulses which we are unable to acknowledge, sensitive areas of which we are unaware until some unexpected stimulus provokes there some extreme pain or pleasure. Indeed why should I speak only of childhood? Am I not myself, who regard myself as a grown man, an excellent example of what is irrational in the mind and involuntary in the will? For both reason and will (so far as they are conscious) deter me from the brutal and degrading spectacles of the arena; yet still I am drawn to them irresistibly.

I know, however, from my own experience in the lecture room at Carthage that only some slight movement or alteration of the mind, the imagination or the affections is required in order to make the will operative in the sense that we consciously desire. It is only then that we feel free; and I suppose that what most distresses me in my present predicament is not so much the fact that I am wasting time on a futile and cruel enthusiasm as the fact that I have ceased to be master of myself.

Now it occurs to me that just as I feel ashamed of my addiction to the amphitheatre, so Augustine may feel ashamed of his devotion to sexual pleasure and that he may have begun to feel this shame from the very beginning of his sexual growth. For in these matters also one seems to be deprived of liberty. The very organ of generation has a life of its own and is not subject, as are one's hands and feet, to the instant determination of the mind. Of course the act of sex in itself is not necessarily degrading; I can see that it can be associated with feelings of tenderness and of real delight. Yet none the less it is often a mere compulsion, a forcing of the spirit away from its real intent. True that my own slavery and infatuation is more serious than that of Augustine; for there can never be anything good or noble in the spilling of blood in sport. But so far as the liberty of the mind is concerned, Augustine is, in this one respect, just as much under compulsion as I am. Indeed he admires me for my immunity here just as much as I admire him for his total indifference to the shows of gladiators.

Personally I think that his admiration is misplaced. It is true that I am somewhat disgusted by the thought of sex and I think that the other day that monk Jerome rather approved of me for this. But this disgust is in itself a form of compulsion and it can be explained not on any rational grounds, but merely as a result of a combination of circumstances over which I had little or no control. If my first physical contact with the opposite sex had been of a more normal kind, it is likely that I should now be as deeply implicated in these pleasures as is Augustine himself. Nearly all the boys I knew had had some sort of sexual experience before they were fourteen or fifteen and I, of course, had plenty of opportunities for doing so too. Most of our slave girls, as I can see now, were very willing to have love affairs with me and so were several married women of my acquaintance. The prettiest ones, however, seemed to expect me to make some sort of an initial move, and I did not know what to do. Somehow, though I

wanted it and though I knew little of it, the act of sex seemed
to me, as it still does, preposterous, frightening, even monstrous. There was something very strange, I thought, about
the structure of the female body and when I thought of
women in their nakedness I would be reminded sometimes
of statues and sometimes of cows. Oddly enough my own
body and the bodies of males generally seemed to me more
rational and less surprisingly designed. Not that I was, or
ever have been, one who enjoys the love of boys or men. This
vice (if it is a vice) is more common, I think, in Rome than in
Africa, but of course it is prevalent enough in Africa and all
through my childhood I was constantly being approached by
elder boys who wanted to kiss or fondle me. Often they would
say that this form of love was something higher, more spiritual and unselfish than the love of women, and they would
quote passages from Plato to bear them out. So far as pure
friendship is concerned, I can see that there may be something in the argument, though it is not impossible to be
friends with a woman; but when, as is so often the case, the
ultimate end is a sharing of the physical pleasures of sex, then
the argument loses much of its force; indeed, strangely as the
bodies of women are constructed, they seem to be better
adapted for the fulfilment of these pleasures. So it was that I
shrank in a kind of horror from the physical endearments of
men. When I thought of these things, I thought of them always in connection with women; yet still I could not reconcile
my desires with my reason or with my sense of propriety.

Now, when I think of Augustine and Lucilla, of Praetextatus and his wife and of many others, admiring, as I do,
their goodness and their warmth as well as their intellectual
powers, I cannot help feeling that in my celibacy I am
missing something of great importance. Nebridius, Augustine
and I have all pledged ourselves to the pursuit of wisdom,
and it is true that many wise men among the Neo-Platonists,
the Manichaeans and even the Christians have declared that
all sexual activity is an impediment in this pursuit. But,

as Augustine has often pointed out, not all wise men have been of this opinion. Socrates was married (though apparently not happily) and even the Christian God is supposed to have performed his first miracle at a marriage ceremony, which seems to imply that in his view there is something natural in the married state. I must reflect that I owe my own existence to the common impulse of my parents. Yet somehow I shrink from imagining my father and mother in the positions necessary for the begetting and conceiving of a child—overcome by the same unreasoning frenzy which I have observed in others and which I have experienced partially and unsatisfactorily myself.

True, this passion has been celebrated by the poets, yet here also the greatest of them (Sophocles and Euripides for example) tend chiefly to emphasize the cruel and destructive aspects of physical love, and among our own writers Lucretius, who was a philosopher as well as a poet, looks upon this agitation of the senses with horror and dismay. I myself cannot think of the act itself without disgust, and this is not because I am cold-hearted. I feel passionately for my friends and tremble with joy when I know that one of them will soon be coming to see me. I follow each smallest expression of the face or modulation of the voice, am delighted by every indication of shared feeling, love the gestures or the mannerisms which I have come to know and am aware of a kind of sweetness, a melting of the heart, when I reflect how fully and totally I can trust and be trusted. Nor are these beautiful and passionate feelings wholly spiritual. I love the bodies, the skin, the hair, the lips and hands of my friends just as much as I love their intellects, their gaiety, their every mood. But this keen physical awareness of them has nothing whatever to do with the movement or inflammation of the sexual organ and as for women I am most at ease with one who is considerably older than myself or who, like Lucilla, is wholly devoted to someone else.

VI

There is certainly an element of fear in this attitude of mine, and it may be, as Augustine has often suggested, that my first and only experience of sex with a woman, disgusting as it was, has affected me unduly. It was at Madaura and towards the end of my school-days. Augustine had already gone on to his advanced studies in Carthage and so had other friends and acquaintances of mine from Thagaste. I was regarded as a good pupil by my masters and was also interested in and proficient at all the games and exercises of our age. One boy in particular (he came from an undistinguished family in Madaura) had attached himself to me in a somewhat servile form of friendship—though friendship is scarcely the word to use of this relationship. He was older and bigger than I was, though curiously not my equal in any of the sports in which we engaged. He was not clever and would listen to my opinions on all intellectual matters with a kind of wonder and respect which, I suppose, flattered me, though I was embarrassed by his real or pretended admiration for the wealth and status of my parents. I can see now that I must have enjoyed finding myself in the position of a leader with at least one apparently devoted follower, and he a boy older than myself. Somehow I have now forgotten his name, though I can remember his appearance well enough. He was tall and fat, with thick lips and a turned-up nose. I used to excuse his coarse looks to myself by reflecting that Socrates also had been ugly. But Socrates was renowned for both charm and intelligence. This boy had neither.

Once, as boys do, we were talking about women and I, wishing to preserve the ascendancy I had over my friend, was pretending to know more of this subject that I did. I laughed at jokes which I never fully understood and presented a mysterious air of secrecy when questioned as to my own experiences, implying, or endeavouring to do so, that they were many and various. I still find it strange that I should have behaved in so ludicrous and hypocritical a manner. I have never been ashamed to admit that I am ignorant of some book which I ought to have read or of some athletic skill which I do not possess; yet here was I asserting, and probably very unconvincingly—though my friend was dull-witted enough—knowledge where ignorance, at my age, would not have been at all discreditable. My friend was telling me of a place he knew in the outskirts of Madaura, where particularly rare pleasures were to be had. 'It's expensive,' he was saying, 'but you have plenty of money, and if you'll pay for me, I'll take you there. You can see, for instance, a woman with a donkey and it's absolutely different when you're in the same room from what it's like when you see it in the theatre. But that costs rather a lot. It's rather a strain on the woman and of course only the old hags do it. They're the only ones big enough.' He looked at me doubtfully and added, 'All the same it's worth seeing.'

By now I felt disgusted but, I must own, I was also aware of a certain excitement. As both my friend and I were attempting to behave like men of the world (as they are called) I dissembled my feelings and told him merely that I did not have money for this entertainment.

He went on to describe other pleasures which were obtainable. I was often shocked by his language, even though there was much of it that I could not understand, but I was pleasantly and in a most novel way stimulated. I was actually glad that I could regard myself as now somehow committed to an experiment from which, with a great part of my nature, I shrank. So I agreed to go with him that evening and to bring with me sufficient money for the two of us.

I passed the rest of that day in a state of strange excitement. With much of my mind I bitterly regretted the decision that had been made. These embraces, whatever they might be, which I was to purchase could not be, for that reason, anything but sordid commodities; and I can never love anything that does not come from the heart. And then I was frightened. This was something which I had not done before and it seemed to me that in this action there must be involved other senses, other aspects of my own personality than those with which I was familiar. Moreover the whole notion that by an extension of my own body I was to enter into the body of a woman was to me bizarre and even cruel, as it might be the infliction of a wound. So I thought, and yet another part of my mind (and almost simultaneously, it seems to me) thought differently and actually revelled in the squalor of its imagination. I recalled with pleasure every obscenity which I had heard or witnessed—the jokes of schoolfellows, the provocative gestures and naked forms of performers in the theatre, and with these I somehow managed to conjoin images from literature—Dido entering the cave with Aeneas, while the nymphs shrieked from the summit of the mountain, Orpheus grasping at a beauty that was vanishing away.

How, in a mind that we are taught to consider rational, can such confusion prevail? How can good and evil, the ugly and the beautiful so coexist? Here, as Augustine says, the Manichees seem to have the likeliest explanation when they assert that we are compounded of seeds or elements of both light and darkness, both equally real. They go on to say that, while it is our duty to try to live according to the light and free the light from darkness, it is inevitable that the darkness will at times overwhelm us and for this we (or the part of us that is light) cannot be blamed. But why then do we feel guilt and shame? No one can be guilty for not avoiding the inevitable. I must remember to ask Augustine about this.

However it may be, by the evening of that day, when I was due to meet my friend, I was more terrified than eager. I almost failed to keep the appointment and on the way to the house where we were going I felt a strong impulse to turn and run away. I was ashamed to do this, but I was unable to resist, when we were actually at the door of the house, confessing to him that in fact this was the first experience of this kind which I had ever had. Perhaps I hoped that at this last moment he might somehow relent, might take half or all the money for himself and let me go away. For now I had lost all desire to impress him with any notion of my superiority. But his reaction was very different. For a moment he stood still in astonishment and then he burst out laughing. 'Splendid,' he said. 'The girls will be delighted. I know what we'll do. We'll have an old Roman wedding and I'll be Priapus.'

I had been told by him previously that these women (one of whom had been, when she was younger, famous in the theatre at Carthage) would often, to add zest to their entertainment, enact various scenes from mythology—Pluto and Proserpine, for example, or Pasiphäe and the bull. Or they might appear dressed in the manner of those Christian women or girls who have pledged themselves to virginity—a procedure which now, so I am told, is common among the prostitutes of Rome. I did not know what was meant by 'an old Roman wedding', but now, having got so far and seeing no hope of turning back, I put on, to the best of my ability, an air of confidence and began soon to feel, together with my trepidation, an excitement and an eagerness which swallowed up all thought and all distinction of ideas.

The room we entered was, for this quarter of the town, furnished with surprising taste and richness. It was brightly lighted and wine was set out on the low tables. It appeared that we were expected, for a tall woman, somewhat past middle age, rose to greet us after the servant had opened the door. Her hair was dyed a flaming red colour and she was well dressed though with too much jewellery. One could see that she had once been beautiful, for traces of beauty remained in her face, though her body had become loose and sagging and her wide mouth with its too thick lips seemed almost as though it did not belong to the high cheekbones and the soft engaging eyes, but to be of another natural order, as it might be the orifice of some sea creature. Her manners were graceful and I was beginning to feel more at my ease, as though this were some ordinary and social occasion, when my friend leaned towards her and began to whisper into her ear, evidently speaking about me. I imagined that he was telling her both that I was possessed of some money and that I was a virgin, for her eyes looked at me first with respect and then with a kind of pleasurable amusement. I found myself blushing and, to hide this fact, I rose from my seat and began to walk about the room, examining the various ornaments upon the walls. When I turned round I found that our hostess was just beside me. She put one arm around my neck and her hand was very soft against my cheek. She turned my head gently towards her, looked for a long time, as it seemed to me, into my eyes and then pressed her lips upon mine. At first the pressure was light but soon I felt as though her lips were enveloping me and, as it were, drawing out of me something from depths of which I had been unconscious. She drew her head away and now her eyes seemed bigger, very serious and at the same time, I thought, almost hungry. I moved clumsily towards her again, but now she laughed gaily and patted me on the cheek. 'No,' she said, 'for your wedding you must have someone younger. And besides (she turned to my friend) I want nothing to do with Priapus.'

She gave an order to the servant, who left the room. Soon the inner door opened again and three girls came in. They astonished me. The first was tall and fair-haired. Her features were regular and firmly made. She had the somewhat narrow mouth and insolently confident expression in the eyes which we often observe in statues of athletes. The upper part of her body was fully clothed in the dress of a charioteer, with leather straps across her breast. She carried a small whip in her hand and below the waist she wore nothing. She glanced at me with a kind of supercilious interest and took her place on one of the couches, leaning back against the cushions and crossing her legs. She took a glass of wine from my friend without looking at him and brushed his hand aside when he attempted to fondle one of her thighs.

She was followed into the room by another girl who was completely naked. Her body, too, was beautiful and it seemed softer than that of the charioteer. I was somehow ashamed to look very closely at her, though I noticed that her pubic hair, unlike that of the charioteer, had been shaved. She came and sat down at my feet, and, as she smiled, she allowed the tip of her tongue to protrude from her lips. I took another glass of wine and remember thinking that the wine was good.

The next to appear was a young girl, somewhat shorter in stature, who was dressed in every respect like one of those Christian nuns whom one sees frequently in Rome, but who are not so often to be met with in Africa. Indeed, I had only seen a very few of them and they were elderly women who used to call on my mother and whom she treated with respect, though my father would allude to them as beggars. This girl behaved, as she came in, in a manner befitting her costume. Her eyes were downcast and she looked neither to the right nor left; but when she had taken her place on a couch, she looked up at me quickly and with a wholly mischievous expression, before turning down her eyes and fingering some beads which she wore round her neck. My friend was standing beside me and whispered into my ear, 'Have her. She's the best of the lot.'

I poured myself another glass of wine and while I did so I could hear, as though from a distance, our hostess speaking. She was telling the girls to behave with becoming modesty as we were going to have an old Roman wedding and I was to choose my bride. For the nun, modesty was easy enough to simulate, but for the charioteer it was something impossible. She contented herself with putting aside her whip and placing a cushion on her lap. The other girl folded her arms across her breasts and looked up into my face with an expression of wounded innocence, as though she had been taken at a disadvantage. I found this expression strangely appealing.

After some more conversation, in which I took little part, and some more wine, I was asked to make my choice of a 'bride'. I had already been considering this matter. The charioteer was, to me, altogether too alarming and I felt chiefly drawn to the nun; but my association of such women with my mother deterred me from making this choice. I therefore chose the girl who was sitting naked at my feet. Our hostess smiled and told the three girls to go and get dressed. 'I,' she said, 'as suits my age, shall be Virginensis; you (she turned to the charioteer) will be Prema and you (indicating the nun) will be Partiunda. And see that Priapus is in a proper condition. Don't let him touch any of you till after the ceremony.'

The girls withdrew, laughing, and my friend went with them. On his way out he winked at me and said, 'You'll have her first, Alypius, but I'd just as soon have my part.'

I was left alone with our hostess and she began to explain to me the details of the performance which was about to take place. I was, of course, familiar with that part of the ceremony of the old religion which goes on publicly—how the bride, in the saffron veil, is escorted through the streets to her husband's house in a procession of torches, with much singing (often of an obscene character), how the husband lifts her over the threshold (a superstitious act which is supposed to avert evil) and how he scatters nuts among the young men in his company. This antique ceremony, dating back no doubt to the earliest years of the republic, is not often carried out nowadays, though it was encouraged among men of wealth in the days of the Emperor Julian and some, in particular those who are most opposed to the Christians, will still insist upon it. Now, however, we were to perform a travesty of the scene which is supposed to take place secretly in the bedroom after all the guests have retired. There are, I was told, either present or assumed to be present three goddesses, whose parts, in the old days, were often taken by respectable matrons. First there is Virginensis, who loosens the virgin girdle of the bride and undresses her. Then there is Prema (the presser down) who holds the bride in position. Partiunda is there to help the husband do his office, 'though,' said our hostess, smiling as she looked at me, 'I don't think you will need much help. And then,' she added, 'when it is all over, the bride, of course, has to pay her respects to Priapus. Otherwise she may be infertile.'

Somehow I felt stimulated rather than amused or disgusted by this account of the ludicrous customs or beliefs of the ancient Romans. Nor was I disturbed by the fact that I found myself to be engaged in some kind of play-acting. I seemed to have been relieved of responsibility and so became more confident and more eager. Had there been anything natural in this affair, any love or tenderness, I should no doubt have felt the kind of shame and diffidence which one must feel whenever one is approaching for the first time any intimacy with another being. But now my body, or rather one part of it, had taken over the reins of control and my mind felt lighter and more vigorous from the very completeness of its subjugation.

The others, now prepared for their parts, came back again into the room. My friend was completely naked and his face had been grotesquely painted so as to imitate one of the more vulgar statues of Priapus. He had thick lips and a snub nose by nature but his mouth had been widened and extended to give him a clown's grin. He reeled as he walked, perhaps confusing the attributes of Priapus with those of Silenus. With one hand he brandished in front of him his swollen penis and with the other he made obscene gestures in the air. He was a disgusting sight, but seemed inordinately pleased with himself. Our hostess, who had now adopted the role of the goddess Virginensis, told him sternly to keep quiet and to seat himself on a slightly raised pedestal in one corner of the room. The very beastliness of his appearance had disturbed me. Again I began to feel frightened and the ardour which a moment before had possessed me was replaced by a kind of chill.

Meanwhile the other two 'goddesses' were escorting my 'bride' towards the bed. On her head she wore the saffron veil and there were golden slippers on her feet. She never raised her eyes to mine, but would sometimes turn her head from side to side, like some innocent animal in a trap from which it knows it cannot escape. In fact her acting was so good that she seemed really to be a frightened virgin about to undergo an experience which was wholly new to her at the hands of a man who had, perhaps, been chosen for her by her parents and whom she had seldom or never seen before. But now some part of my mind had become awake and in spite of the excellence of her acting I was aware that our roles were, in a sense, completely reversed. She was engaged in an action which, from countless repetition, was perfectly familiar to her; it was I who was the virgin, who found myself here partly against my will and who, after some moments of confidence, seemed now, as in a dream, moving with trepidation in some landscape or city utterly unknown to me, fearful of every step I took, yet still strangely impelled to go forward.

Virginensis now moved forward and solemnly removed the saffron veil from the girl's head. She then unloosed the girdle and with a quick movement stripped her of the one garment which she was wearing. The girl in her nakedness looked up at me timidly, as though imploring mercy. She attempted clumsily to cover her breasts and secret parts with her hands. Somehow I was wholly carried away by this exhibition. I forgot the presence of my disgusting friend in the corner; I forgot that all this show was nothing but acting. I passionately desired the girl's body, as though for years I had been longing for it and for it alone. And this fierce desire was accompanied even by a form of tenderness. I wanted not only to possess but somehow to protect this girl whom I had never seen before and would never see again. But no element of past or future was before my mind. There was nothing but the present.

The 'Goddess' Prema now took the girl's feebly resisting body firmly in her hands and laid her on the bed. She seemed to be attempting to writhe away from the powerful grip and to bury her face in the cushions, but the other 'goddess', standing behind her head, took her arms and held them fast, while Prema spread her legs wide apart. By now I had thrown my clothes aside and had soon entered into this body which I so frantically desired. I was aware of the girl moaning as though in pain, and now I was savagely gripping her arms myself and forcing her head round to meet my lips. The final action was soon over and I felt all round me a delicious warmth, a satisfaction unlike and greater than any I had ever known. My limbs relaxed and those feelings of savagery which a second before had wholly overwhelmed me melted away and were replaced by the purest feelings of tenderness and of gratitude. I wanted to be and indeed for the moment fancied that I was alone with this other being into whom I had penetrated and from whom I had derived such joy and so indescribable a peace. I had forgotten where I was and wished to remain forgetful. This dream was to me a perfect reality and the real voices and actions which dispelled it seemed to me at first dreamlike, impossible or monstrous.

The girl was pushing me away from her. The expression of her face had now changed entirely, so that there was nothing modest in it at all. She patted me lightly on the cheek. 'Not bad,' she said, 'but you were too quick. You can try again when I've finished with Priapus.' I was aware of my friend shouting out that she was to hurry. Virginensis was pulling at my shoulder and I attempted to shake her off, just as one will shake aside the hand of one who is waking one from a deep sleep. I felt outraged and alarmed as though I were (and indeed I was) in some company whose conventions and manners were wholly unlike any with which I was familiar.

The girl slid away from beneath me. I made some sort of a gesture as though to hold her back, but the body of which I had felt the warmth and, as it seemed to me, the essence was going from me, losing what I had conceived to be its identity, and becoming something else and something alien, undergoing, as it were, the kind of transformation we experience in the vision of some dreadful dream in which a face which we know and love will suddenly put on another and a dreadful expression utterly unlike reality, and yet we know it is the same face.

The three 'goddesses' were leading the girl towards the seated figure of Priapus, who was waving his arms about in a ridiculous manner and shouting out obscenities to her. She leaned forward and for a moment or two took his extended penis in her mouth. Then the other three lifted her from the ground and placed her upon him in a sitting posture so that he entered into her. He gripped her neck with one of his huge hands, pulled her head towards him and began to lick her lips and nostrils with long strokes of the tongue, like some great dog. The other hand was wildly kneading her buttocks. She herself was writhing from side to side, pinching the flesh of his arms and flanks and uttering gasps of a frenzied excitement and delight. Both their bodies were streaming with sweat. The three other women stood looking on intently. Their eyes were interested and critical like those of spectators at the games.

As for me, I was not conscious of any thought at all. I was simply overwhelmed with horror. I rapidly put my clothes on, threw my purse on a table and made for the door. There was some attempt to stop me, but I do not know what the women said or what were the words my friend shouted after me. I was afraid to run through the streets in case I might be taken for a thief, but though I walked slowly I was still unable to think at all rationally, nor have I ever until this day attempted to recall in consecutive detail the incidents of the evening. Always the details have been submerged in one or two powerful impressions—the nearness and the delight of yielding flesh, a feeling of inexpressible tenderness, and then the horrible grinning Priapus-face.

VII

Last night I sat up late writing down that account of my experience in the brothel at Madaura. I slept very well, but before I went to sleep it occurred to me to wonder why it was that, after having kept for so long the details of this incident buried, as it were, and in a fragmentary state in some recess of my memory, I should have chosen this particular moment to recall them. I remember that all yesterday, from time to time, I would find myself stirred by feelings of shame and self-reproach at my behaviour at the games, at the imagination of what Augustine or Nebridius would think of me if they had seen me there, and of despair at what seemed to me the compulsion of my infatuation. Now suddenly it crossed my mind that I had no longer any desire to visit the games, but I smiled at this thought, as it seemed too good to be true. I had tired myself out with writing and I soon fell asleep.

But when I woke late this morning the same thought immediately presented itself to me and I found with astonishment that I was now recalling my previous behaviour almost dispassionately. I was disgusted at it, certainly, but in my disgust there was no longer any element of fascination. I might almost have been considering the actions of someone else, except that I knew they were my own. This new and, as it seemed, involuntary orientation of my mind delighted me and I was afraid of attempting to analyse it, lest it might vanish and be replaced by the madness which I knew. I took up some books of law and of philosophy which I had long laid aside, and I found that I was reading them with unusual care and tranquillity. When my friends came to call for me on the way to the games, I told them that I would not go and I could scarcely believe the sound of my own voice speaking these words not defiantly or desperately, but with the certain knowledge that I had not even the slightest wish to go. Naturally my friends were surprised. They asked me what on earth had happened to me since yesterday. Had I lost money? Had I become a Christian? And all I could reply was 'Nothing' or 'I don't know'. There was a good deal of laughter and bets were exchanged on how long my resolution would last; but when they had gone, I felt strangely that the word 'resolution' was altogether wrong. I was making no conscious effort. It was rather as though I had come round from some fever, except that I felt neither weak nor light-headed.

I ask myself how this abrupt change had come about. The common opinion is that when we are tempted to commit some criminal or immoral act, it is our duty to exercise, by means of our will, control over our passions. Yet this was just what I have been attempting to do and my efforts proved wholly ineffectual. The calm and peace of mind which I now feel has come about in some quite different, and to me mysterious, way. Is it the fact, then, that this capacity for self-control, which every child is encouraged to cultivate, only exists when it is unnecessary, when, that is to say, the temptation has not, in reality, any great appeal to us? But if this were so, how can it happen, as has just happened to me, that one is relieved from an overwhelming temptation as it were automatically and with no effort of the will at all? It occurs to me that some, at least, of the Christians believe that man is in himself wholly weak and sinful and is unable to act rightly except through the power given to him by their God. Of course the notion that Gods can directly help a man is not a new one. It is common in Homer, though in Homer the heroes are certainly not represented as weak and powerless beings. They are less powerful than the Gods, but they are almost of the same species, only differing because of their mortality, and this very difference gives them a strength and dignity of their own. It seems to me that the Christian view of the essential weakness of man without God does no justice to the real dignity of man. Moreover though they talk much of their total dependence on a spiritual power and of the worthlessness of human and worldly endeavour, there is not much evidence that they really believe this themselves. They seem to me to be as a rule as ambitious as other men, and, as Praetextatus pointed out the other evening, their bishops often live in greater state than is to be found anywhere outside the court of the emperor. They are, indeed, great adepts at holding at one and the same time positions which cannot be logically reconciled. They claim to believe that the world will very shortly, perhaps to-day or tomorrow, come to an end, and yet they behave and are organized as though convinced it will last for ever. They have a God who is also a man, and then they add two other Gods and go on to maintain that these three Gods are really one. So in this question of how we can behave with justice and honour and not be carried away, as I have been, by impulses which are against our truest nature, their explanation appears to beg more questions than it answers. If man can do nothing good entirely by his own efforts, then man is essentially irresponsible; he can be neither tragic nor heroic. Yet the Christians insist on personal responsibility in the smallest details of their lives and their mythology is full of stories of their heroes, whom they call saints or martyrs and whom they admire for just those qualities of fortitude and endurance which, according to their view of the abject nature of man, they could not really possess, since they are qualities imparted to them from the outside.

And yet I must own that this freedom which I now have from my temptation to demean myself by a savage enjoyment is something for which I can scarcely claim the credit myself. True, I struggled against it, but my struggles appeared unavailing. I did not pray to the Christian God, nor am I conscious of any God's intervention.

The Manichaeans certainly make more sense than the Christians. Their theories are complex but not, like those of the Christians, wholly irrational. They admit what seems to

be a fact known to us from experience, that we are compounded of elements of both good and evil and they will
admit too that there must be occasions when the elements of
evil will so predominate that they are bound to overwhelm
the elements of good. When this happens, we cannot strictly
be blamed for what takes place. It remains our duty to constantly endeavour by meditation, by fasting and by the use of
the correct diet to rid ourselves of those dark elements and to
give scope for the light. So far, it seems, the Manichaean view
does at least conform to our experience, though the theological, or cosmological, background to their theories seems
to me to be in many ways at least as fanciful as that of the
Christians. They avoid the absurdity of believing in a God
who is also a man, presumably with limbs and senses like
others, and they admit the existence of a real and independent
power of evil whereas the Christians maintain that their God
not only created everything but is also all-powerful—which
must mean that he is responsible for evil as well as good. But
how can one believe this of a being whom one is expected to love
and worship? There is much beauty, too, in the Manichaean
view of nature, for they encourage us to believe that everywhere in the universe the same struggle continues between
light and darkness that we observe in ourselves. Stars and
constellations, the sun and the moon, flowers, animals and
birds seem to be more vitally connected with us than in the
more arid cosmogonies of either the Jews or the Christians.
This, I remember, was what interested me most when
Augustine first talked to me about the Manichees in Carthage.
I felt the universe to be both vast and mysterious and I felt
(and still feel) myself to be a weak and undecided being in the
midst of it. I wanted to find a religion which would both
accord with my apprehension of the beauty, the variety, and
the terror around me, and would also give me a confidence
and an understanding which I lacked. No religion I knew of
satisfied these demands. The stories of the Greeks are beautiful, but owe their beauty to the skill of poets rather than to

any logical coherence. Even before Plato the best philosophers had either rejected them or interpreted them out of existence. And as for our Roman mythology, it is, where it differs from that of the Greeks, much less beautiful and even more senseless. It is, in fact, quite childish. We even have Gods and Goddesses whose concern is the process of excretion. I had certainly, as a child, been impressed with what my mother told me of the Christian faith, but even then it appeared to me to be narrow as well as obscure. There was no place in it for the stars, the flowers and trees and all the infinite variety of the world.

And so I was delighted and enthralled when Augustine first explained to me the views of the Persian, Mani, and of how he taught that all creation is alive and sensitive as we are, of the intimate feelings which exist in trees and plants and of the splendours of the sky, the great wheel of the zodiac pouring the liberated light into the reservoirs of sun and moon, and of how we all, according to our capacities, can share in this work of liberation. There seemed to me in these doctrines a colour, a grace, a scope which I had found nowhere else. I was impressed too by what was known of Mani himself, of his travels through Asia, India and China, and of how, though he called himself 'the Ambassador of Light' or 'the Paraclete', he admitted the existence of other prophets and teachers before himself, and did not assert that one man or one people must be the one repository of truth. In his system there is a place for the Christian God, Jesus, but it is declared that he, being an emanation of the divine, could not possibly have been fettered and confined in the physical limits of sense and space; he could not have suffered and he could not have died. It would be more proper to conceive of him as a kind of phantom, taking on a human appearance for his own purposes and then returning to the Light from which he came.

I used to be greatly attracted by these doctrines and, I suppose, still am in a way. But I cannot see how they can explain wholly my present state of mind. It can be said, and in a sense truly, that when I felt that sudden and insane passion for the games, my mind was clouded over by those elements of Darkness which are always there and that subsequently the elements of Light have succeeded in breaking through and, as it were, clearing the sky of my consciousness. This is, in part, what it feels like. But am I then just a patient battle ground for opposing forces, neither of which I can influence or control? And if so, can I be said to exist except as an object to be scrutinized from outside? And yet I appear to be able to scrutinize myself and am able, unlike an animal or a plant, to set down in intelligible language some of the result of my self-scrutiny. May it not be, I wonder, that what we call our will operates, or can operate, at a much deeper level than that of which we are conscious and that 'self-control' is really exercised not directly, but indirectly? Certainly I did wish to control myself. I did have a horror of my own behaviour. Yet this attempt at control and this genuine horror were quite ineffective. I enjoyed doing what I did not want to do. I was disgusted with myself for my happiness, yet was still happy in spite of my disgust. Though perhaps 'happiness' is not the word. I am really happy now, when I am doing what I wanted to do.

It seems to me that my will, which could achieve nothing at the time, must still have been operative somewhere beneath the surface of my consciousness and must have discovered there a source of strength of which I was unaware. Yet again the metaphor of strength is unsatisfactory, for there seems to have been no strain, no effort of any kind. I am reminded of what sometimes happens in the course of literary composition, when we attempt vainly to find the right word or the right phrase to express something; and we do not really know what the 'something' is until we have found the phrase or the word which will give it shape. Often, after a long struggle, we give up in despair or else try to be content with some other word or phrase which in fact we know to be inappropriate or positively misleading. And then, by some apparent accident (we may be aimlessly watching the movements of a leaf or thinking of something quite different), the words we are looking for come easily and quickly and we know in the flash of a moment both what we wanted to say and how to say it. And yet without the preliminary and quite unsuccessful effort we might never have known either the meaning of or the expression for what was in our minds.

In my present case it was not a question of finding either meaning or expression, but rather of being able to act as I wanted to act. I felt (and at first could scarcely believe the feeling to be genuine) that I had this ability just before I went to sleep last night; and in the hours before going to sleep I had not been thinking of my predicament at all. I had been writing down (and again I do not know what impelled me to do this) for the first time an account of that experience of mine in Madaura, from the memory of which I had always previously shrunk back, just as we often shrink from recalling occasions where we have behaved dishonourably or made fools of ourselves. When such occasions come into our mind, it seems to back away from them, sweating and trembling, like a horse confronted by an unknown danger or an insuperable obstacle at which still his rider is urging him. Last night for the first time I did not feel this uncontrollable panic. Some people, no doubt, would explain this by saying that I have now outgrown a boyish, or infantile, sense of shame and have become able to accept what are sometimes called 'the facts of life'. But it is not this at all. I still know that it is shameful and sordid to go to such places. I am still puzzled and alarmed by a powerful and savage instinct in myself and I am still horrified by the much greater and quite unrelieved savagery which I observed in the grinning Priapus-figure of my friend and in the gestures and expression of the girl who, in this absurd parody, had been my 'bride'. But I also see now (though I was certainly not aware of seeing it when I was writing down the description of that incident) that there is a similarity, and perhaps a connection, between what is violent and bestial in the act of sex and the savage excitement that is felt by spectators of the shows of gladiators or of the slaughter of wild animals or criminals. This indeed is common knowledge, though I have never reflected on it before. According to my friends it is much easier to seduce a woman directly after she has been attending one of these shows than at any other time, and they themselves, when sated with the sight and smell of blood and all the excitement of the arena, feel it particularly necessary to complete the day either with their mistresses or in a brothel. So it is evident that savagery, bestiality and even cruelty are, or may be, a part of sexual desire.

But I remembered also, and with more clarity than ever before, that in that experience of mine at Madaura there was present a quite different element and one that never does and never could enter into the consciousness of a spectator at the games. I remembered these few moments of extraordinary peace, confidence, security and tenderness which came after my purely physical impulse had been expended. During those moments I had, irrational and impossible as it may seem, almost or entirely ceased to believe that I was in fact playing a part in a charade designed to stimulate me, to gratify my friend and to make money for the establishment. The body which I had enjoyed I loved and this love (for there is no other word for it) was one (though again this seems impossible) of a singular purity. And I saw that what had really shocked and offended me was not so much my own action and passions— my gaucheness, the uncontrollable impulses of my flesh, the elimination of my rational powers—as my discovery that this feeling was not shared by the girl or, indeed, by anyone else. Of course I could not possibly have expected it to be, yet still the fact that it was not was what had shocked and upset me much more than any particular exhibition of the coarse and brutal nature of my friend, which I knew already. My disappointment had been such that, until last night, I had confused everything together. Everything to do with sex filled me with dismay. When I was with good and admirable people like Praetextatus and his wife I shrank back from the thought that their calm, their courtesy and their intelligence must often have been disturbed by emotions and actions the thought of which filled me with horror. And though I know Augustine and Lucilla much more intimately I usually try to avoid any discussion with Augustine on that aspect of their life together which he, for his part, often wants to talk about.

Now it seems to me that I have become enlightened in two important ways simply through the fact that, for some reason which I do not understand, I have acquired a new clarity of memory so that I can recall in detail, in order and in proportion my acts and feelings on that occasion in Madaura. In the first place, though I can still see nothing beautiful in that abdication of reason and those contortions of frenzied bodies which seem inseparable from the act of sex, I can now recognize that they can be accompanied by and may even be the condition for a state of mind which can rightly be called beautiful. I still find this fact puzzling, but I can admit the fact, whereas previously I had, owing to the faulty and confused nature of my recollections, regarded every sexual act as being necessarily cruel, ugly, shameful and degrading. And in the second place I can see that those elements of cruelty, savagery and filth which my memory had presented to me as being specifically sexual are, though in a different context, just the very things which have excited me and swept away reason and decency during my enjoyment of the shows of gladiators, with the immensely important difference that here there was no redeeming feature of any kind; here there was nothing which could conceivably be called good or beautiful. And so, while I can now think more calmly and even with a certain understanding (though this is still difficult) of the sexual behaviour of my friends, all the fear and horror which I used to feel at the imagination of such actions has become, as it were, transferred to my memory and imagination of the performances in the arena. So far from being any more attracted to them, I am revolted by the very thought of them.

But I still do not know why and from what unknown recesses of my mind arose the impulse and ability to clarify my memory and to effect this transference. I prayed to no God and I had discovered with shame that my own will, or 'better nature' as we call it, was quite ineffective. I should like to think that my will can continue to operate when I am no longer conscious of it or even that some God is guiding me. But how can I test the truth of either of these propositions when the evidence for either the one or the other is beyond my reach? Or was everything caused, as an Epicurean might suggest, by some slight movement of one of those invisible atoms which control or constitute my mind? Should I not be content, seeing that I have reached, by whatever means, the state of mind which I wished to reach? Indeed this makes me happy, but unless I have some understanding, I cannot be content.

VIII

Today my friends again called on me to ask me to accompany them to the games and again I had not the least difficulty in refusing them. This time they did not take my refusal so hardly, possibly because they themselves had been disappointed by the performances yesterday. It appears that what had been advertised as the great attraction for the day had turned out to be a total failure. Thirty or forty crocodiles had been produced by the organizers of the games and these beasts were to fight with men armed only with small wooden daggers and with little room in which to manœuvre. It had been anticipated that a number of these men would be killed and devoured by the crocodiles, but that, if a sufficient number survived, they would be likely to kill all the crocodiles in the end. Large sums of money had been bet on the final result and on the numbers of survivors. Things, however, had not turned out as expected. As soon as the crocodiles had been released from their cages it had been evident that they were in poor condition and it was afterwards rumoured, or discovered, that for more than thirty days previously they had refused to eat. Now they showed only the feeblest activity and after a number of them had been stabbed in the eyes, overturned and stabbed again in their bellies without making any resistance at all, the crowd had become furious and demanded their withdrawal. There had been fighting all round the arena, some demanding payment of their bets and others refusing to pay up on the grounds that the contest had been an unfair one. It had taken some hours to restore order and after that the promoters of the games had had little else to offer except a hunt of antelopes which, my friends said, was skilfully enough done, but had not been what the audience had come to see. I knew from my own experience that what the audience had come to see was bloodshed and brutality. Exhibitions of skill were only pleasing by way of intermissions in the excitement of deeper passions. The whole recital of events filled me with disgust, though I was aware that only two days ago I should have been thinking and talking exactly as my friends were thinking and talking now.

When my friends had left me I turned, again with a calm and energetic mind, to the study of my law books, but I was soon, and most agreeably, interrupted by receiving a letter from my friend Nebridius. He writes from his estate near Carthage, but he goes to the city frequently and, as usual, had been seeing much of Augustine. Nebridius has, I think, wider interests than any of us. He is not only a keen student of philosophy, literature and mathematics but, unlike most people in Africa who are not personally engaged in government service, follows military and political events with care and interest. There was a time when he was thinking seriously of making a career for himself either in the army or in administration and he has not only the ability, but the wealth and personal charm, to be exceedingly successful as a public figure. I think that he abandoned this project largely because of the disgust which he, and indeed all of us, felt at the disgrace and execution of the great Count Theodosius, who had suppressed one of the most dangerous revolts that Africa had ever known and who appeared to be on the point of at least ridding the province of the military governor, Romanus, who for years had oppressed rich and poor alike, and, as was common knowledge, had actively aided the revolt in order to acquire more money and retain still some authority for himself. Leading citizens had complained over and over again to the court at Milan of the extortions and treachery of this governor, but over and over again Romanus had bribed every representative who had been sent out to inquire into his conduct. Now at last Count Theodosius, with the prestige he had won by crushing first a dangerous revolt in Britain and then another one in Africa, seemed certain to see that justice was done. But to the dismay of everyone except the immediate circle of Romanus and the Christian sect of Donatists whom he had supported, a charge of treason had been brought against Theodosius himself and, just after he had been baptized in the orthodox Christian Church, he was executed at Carthage. The authors of this appalling act of injustice were the ministers of the young Emperor Gratian, but Gratian himself, who may have known little or nothing about it, was finally responsible and, in spite of his youth and his victories, has never been popular in Africa since. Nebridius had taken this event more hardly than any of us, perhaps because he had been less cynical about politics previously than we had been.

He had fervently believed that great goodness and great power could not only go together but prevail against envy, corruption, self-seeking, intrigue and superstition, had been fond of quoting to me examples from history which seemed to prove his point and had seemed to us strangely, and rather amusingly, incapable of dealing with the far more frequent examples which we could adduce to prove just the opposite. For on the whole we in Africa are not impressed by what is known as a great general or a great statesman. We have a rich country and we have suffered more than we have gained in war. Countries like Britain and Germany seem very remote from us and there are long periods, I should guess, when the ordinary man in the street does not even know the name of the reigning emperor. We are more concerned with the extortion of local tax collectors than in distant struggles for supreme power. Nebridius is the only African I know, apart from those who hold important positions in the government, who is really interested in imperial politics. And he had retained this interest although, ever since the judicial murder of Count Theodosius, his reaction to political events has been angry, bitter and disillusioned. Every aspect of that case was disgraceful, but there was one in particular which aroused the contempt of Nebridius. It was reported at the time (and there seems no reason to doubt the truth of the report) that one of the principal charges against Theodosius was concerned with a magical experiment which had been made some time previously in Antioch or in one of the cities of the East. The letters of the alphabet had been arranged in a circle and above these was suspended a gold ring, the cord to which it was attached being held by an eminent magician. He claimed, of course, that either his hand or the movement of the cord was controlled by supernatural powers and he had, I believe, a great reputation for being able not only to summon up the spirits of the dead but also to produce the Gods themselves in visible forms. How such a performance can have been taken seriously by a Christian emperor who was supposed not to believe in the ancient Gods at all is something difficult to understand, but it seems that ever since the times of the Emperor Julian who, while rejecting the superstitions of the Christians in the name of Hellenism, was himself the victim of all those superstitions of magic and astrology which Plato or Aristotle would have viewed either with abhorrence or amusement, magicians, astrologists, theurgists and necromancers have, in spite of some occasional official proscription, enjoyed a great vogue. This experiment with the ring is a case in point. It was said that when the question was asked 'Who is aspiring to become emperor?', the ring spelt out the letters THEO and then ceased, apparently because the spirits either could not spell or were uncertain of what the full name was. However, even the first four letters were judged to be useful evidence, despite the fact that there must be hundreds of thousands of people in the empire whose names begin in this way. Several important ministers and generals in the East had already lost their lives because of this unlucky prefix, and the same prefix was brought forward as evidence, and indeed the only evidence, for the treachery of Count Theodosius.

We were all of us, of course, shocked by this story, though some of us, perhaps, were inclined also, no doubt from the thought of an intellectual superiority which we supposed that we possessed, to smile at a form of superstition which was not our own. But Nebridius was more than shocked. He had had, I think, higher hopes than any of the rest of us had bothered to entertain and he was correspondingly the more deeply disappointed. 'What sort of a world is this', I remember him saying, 'in which we live? We have greater wealth, larger and more efficient armies, quicker means of transportation, a better integrated administration, a wider system of education than ever before. We can still produce honest men, good generals, far-sighted administrators. Yet what is happening? We are sick and rotten at the core. In the past whatever was good was upheld and supported and could draw energy from a general respect for virtue and a genuine patriotism. Now virtue is never respected for itself, but only if its reputation can be used as an advertisement for some particular sect or party. Look at the Christians. Will any Catholic (as they call themselves) Christian admit that any of the people whom they call heretics can be good? Of course not. And yet it is well known that many of these "heretics", whether they are intellectually misguided or not, live good lives and are sincere in their beliefs. And as for patriotism, where will you find it? Certainly not in Rome or in Carthage or in Constantinople. For our generals nowadays are usually Franks or Goths or Arabs, many of whom can scarcely speak our language, and the genuine Romans (if there are any) are more interested in the games or in making money or in absurd disputes over trifling points of theology than they are in the security of the frontiers, of which they know nothing, or in justice, which they believe (and rightly) can be bought and sold like anything or anybody else. Personally, I am not in the least surprised that so many uneducated people, and even quite a number of educated ones, believe that the world is coming to an end, that it will be destroyed by fire or that all life is gradually losing vitality, or that some pestilential vapours from outer space are secretly corrupting our minds and our bodies. Of course such an idea is pure mythology. There is no scientific evidence to support any of these contentions. It seems to me more likely that we are somehow, and without being quite conscious of it, determined to destroy ourselves. True that people will cling more rapaciously than ever before to their lives, their property and their social positions. But this is not a sign of confidence in life or of generous ambition; it is a sign of fear and of despair. What people want is not life, but some kind of security against torture and death for themselves, though they are quite prepared to inflict torture and death on others. They cannot even bear to think that they may die—even those who keep on proclaiming that life is not worth living. Nearly everyone is trying to insure himself as immortal. Anyone who can afford it will get washed in the blood of a ram or bull, or go through the long and exhausting initiations into the mysteries of Isis. Probably the reason why the Christians have won so much power and influence is that they offer immortality on cheaper terms than anyone else. Personally, if one cannot live with hope and with generosity, I would rather die and have done with it. But where is there any hope and how can one be generous without being destroyed?'

None of these views, of course, was new to us and probably we had heard them expressed better and more coherently before. But Nebridius spoke with such an extraordinary vehemence and passion that none of us ventured to take him lightly. We were all sorry for him and many of us had an uneasy feeling that something in what he was saying was true. It may well be, I thought, that there has never been a time when people of sincerity and of high ideals have not inveighed against the corruption of the age. Yet Nebridius was right in pointing to a particular kind of debility in our age which would be hard to parallel in previous periods of history. The old forms were still there. In Rome, so we were told, the Vestal Virgins still tended the undying fire; triumphal processions still wound their way up the slopes of the Capitol as in the days of the Scipios or of Julius Caesar; the statues of Gods—Jupiter, Minerva and the rest—still watched over the forum. Yet except among a very small and diminishing number of people these relics of the past had become completely meaningless. Even among the senators probably about half were Christians, though they seemed somehow capable of combining the Christian belief that the old Gods were really demons with the aristocratic convention that they were also beneficent influences on the fortunes of Rome. And the emperor himself was to most people a being far removed from real life. For at least a generation no emperor had visited Rome. Indeed the ordinary person would, according to his tastes, be more interested in the fortunes of a charioteer, a gladiator, an actor, a rhetorician or a bishop than in what happened in the distant courts of Milan, Trèves, Constantinople or wherever an emperor might be. Nebridius was right, then, in saying that, in the old sense, patriotism was dead. We still read the works of Cicero and admired his style and dexterity. But this was all we admired. The passions of his times seemed to us in many ways childish and certainly long out of date. Even in Virgil what we admired, apart from the beauty of his verse, was not his attempt to glorify a patriotic virtue of which he must have found very few examples even in his own times, but rather his pity for the general lot of man, his understanding of misguided passion and his pathetic intimations that, after all, life might not be worth living. And, as Nebridius had pointed out, while what was old and venerable in our culture was, though it remained the basis of our education, dying, what was new was hopelessly confused, inconsistent and, from its very variety, amorphous and ineffective.

Yet still it seemed to me that the desire to know the causes of things, a desire so reluctantly abandoned by Virgil, was not an unworthy one. Archimedes had said, 'Give me the right place to stand, and from there I will move the earth.' There was no such place, but still he invented the principle of the lever. We too indeed had no place to stand, yet perhaps we could accomplish something without falling into apathy and despair.

So I thought then and so I still think, though I own that I have accomplished nothing. Some years have passed now since the time when Augustine, Nebridius and myself decided to devote ourselves deliberately to the pursuit of wisdom, and Nebridius has been at least as active in this as any of us. He has enjoyed certain advantages since he is rich and has little practical work to do except in the management of his estate, with which he is familiar, whereas Augustine and I—Augustine from necessity and also, I think, from a certain ambition, I largely in order to please my parents—have had to give much of our time to our careers. There are times, I think, when with a portion of his mind Nebridius actually envies us for this, for a successful lawyer and a successful professor of rhetoric can attain important positions in the empire and Nebridius, in spite of his cynicism on the subject, still follows politics and the history of the times with much more attention than Augustine or I do. In fact the letter I have just had from him starts, characteristically enough, with his reflections on events which I have scarcely bothered even to consider.

He comments in particular on the change of opinion in Africa with regard to the young Emperor Gratian. He has now, according to Nebridius, suddenly become extremely popular among the Catholic Christians, though he is correspondingly unpopular among the almost equally numerous sect of Donatists. This is an exact reversal of the state of opinion of some few years ago after the execution of Count Theodosius. This event was followed by one of the greatest military disasters in Roman history, when the emperor of the East, Valens, the uncle of Gratian, was defeated and killed by the Goths at Hadrianople. They say that two-thirds of all the eastern armies were destroyed in this battle. The Goths marched unmolested to the walls of Constantinople itself and, had they possessed any skill in siege-craft might have actually taken it, so few were the defenders. I remember at the time that Nebridius spoke with contempt of the attitude taken up by the Christians with regard to this catastrophe. Rome had suffered no such disaster since the times of Hannibal and Cannae. Constantinople might seem far away, but the fact was that the defences of the East were down and, though Gratian had an intact army under his command, it was not inconceivable that the Goths might turn westward towards Italy and Gaul. Yet there were many Christians who appeared to be actually pleased with what had happened. They attributed the defeat not to the incompetence of Valens and his generals (for it seems that the army, in a hopeless position, had fought well to the last) but to a salutary intervention of their God designed to punish Valens for his support of the Arian heresy, which differs from the orthodox creed in attributing to the Son rather less of divinity than to the Father. This view, heartless and irresponsible as it was in regard both to the death and suffering of so many country-men and to the extreme danger of the times, was also, as Nebridius pointed out, logically inept. For if Valens had him-self been tinged with Arianism, there were at least thousands of orthodox Catholics in his defeated army; whereas the victorious Goths, in so far as they were Christian at all, were Arians to a man. However, in the minds of the Catholics of the West neither pity for their co-sectarians nor the claims of simple logic could outweigh the fury that they felt at the recent successes in the capital of the East of a body of Chris-tian opinion which differed in certain respects very slightly from their own.

At this critical time Gratian, now the only effective Roman emperor (since his young brother Valentinian II was still a child of five) had acted magnanimously and, as seems certain, with admirable judgment. He had summoned the son of Count Theodosius, who bears the same name as his father, from his retirement in Spain and had given him first the command of the East and then the title of co-emperor. But what, according to Nebridius, has so pleased the Catholics in Africa in the conduct of Gratian was not this generous action, which did something to atone for the injustice perpetrated on Theodosius' father, and not even the great abilities shown in the East by Theodosius himself in a series of skilful cam-paigns, sometimes in co-operation with Gratian, by which any immediate danger from the Goths seems to have been averted. To all this, apparently, they are indifferent. What chiefly delighted them with regard to Theodosius was that, in the course of a severe illness, he was baptized by a Catholic bishop and in so doing deliberately affronted the Arians. And what pleased them in Gratian is not his military victories nor his act of generosity. It is simply that he has been the first of the emperors to decline the title of pontifex maximus, that he has ordered the statue of Victory to be removed from the senate-house in Rome, and that he has either reduced or abolished the salaries paid to the Vestal Virgins. In both these actions he had been guided, apparently, by his complete submission, so far as religious affairs go, to the counsel of Ambrose, the Bishop of Milan, who, by all accounts, is not only the most capable, but the most scholarly and eloquent of the bishops in the West. I remember that Praetextatus spoke highly of him, even though he was bitterly opposed to these restrictive measures placed upon the old religion. As Nebridius says, though the objects of a particular and most violent hatred among Christians are their fellow-Christians who belong to different sects, they are at least united in a common detestation of the old Gods in the name of whom they have certainly from time to time suffered some persecution, though probably not so much as they have inflicted, when in a position to do so, on their own co-religionists. Consequently Gratian is now extremely popular in Africa.

He asks me whether he is equally popular in Rome as he has heard rumours that this is not the case. I think that these rumours are certainly true. He has offended the majority of the nobility by his persecution (though his actions scarcely deserve that name) of the old religion and, more important, he has lost the great popularity which he used to have among the army. In his early youth he was undoubtedly a brave and competent commander. Now, so I am told, though he is still young, he seems to have lost all interest in the troops with which he has won victories and even in warfare itself. Instead he has developed a passion for barbarians, for hunting and for the games. His particular favourites are a savage tribe of Scythians and on many occasions he actually goes about in public dressed in furs and carrying, instead of the Roman sword, the Scythian long bow. Large parts of Gaul and Germany have been set aside for him as hunting preserves and for weeks on end he will disappear with his barbarian bodyguard and then make a kind of triumphal return, displaying the carcases of slaughtered beasts or caged live specimens of wolves, bears, boars and elks with as much pride as if he were celebrating a victory in war. He also makes appearances in the amphitheatre, again usually in Scythian or in German dress, and prides himself now, not on his generalship, but on being a better swordsman than the average trained gladiator. This, it seems, is the man who is so lauded as the defender of the Catholic faith. But his way of life is well known here and it appears that even among the Catholic Christians all the credit for the support he gives them is attributed, rightly enough, to the Bishop of Milan, to whom Gratian is probably quite content to leave every decision of a religious character. They say that Ambrose has composed a treatise on the doctrine of the Trinity for the emperor's own use and enlightenment, but he sounds to me too intelligent a man to imagine that Gratian would read or could understand it. Meanwhile there are already rumours of a revolt in Britain led by Maximus, a competent soldier who has served with Theodosius and who is said to enjoy the confidence of the army.

Nebridius will be surprised when I tell him that, to the best of my knowledge, no one in Rome is particularly interested in whether there is a revolt or not or whether or not it will be successful—though perhaps here I should exclude at least some of the Christians, since Maximus is believed to have no strong feelings about any kind of religion.

However, what excites me about Nebridius' letter is not so much his political comments and his inquiries, which I shall do my best to answer. Of course I read all this first part of his letter with interest and enjoyment, but I felt an almost inexpressible delight when, towards the end, I came to the sentence 'I should not be surprised if you were to see Augustine in Rome soon'. For a moment I passed over these words, reading them again and again, since the news seemed to be too good to be true. Then I read on hurriedly and found that it is indeed the case that Augustine plans, as soon as he can, to leave Carthage and set up as a teacher in Rome. He is becoming, so Nebridius says, more and more disgusted with the manners of the students in Carthage and with their generally low standards of learning. I am not surprised at this. For a long time it has been a convention in Carthage that if one pays one's fees to one professor, this entitles one also to visit the classes of other professors. And, as only a minority of students are serious in the pursuit of learning or anxious to qualify as scholars themselves, there are always large numbers who are looking for variety or entertainment rather than education. They will occasionally break up classes of professors who are for some reason unpopular with them, or, at the best, they will burst into another professor's class, listen to what is going on for half an hour or so, and then go on somewhere else. This kind of behaviour is not tolerated in Rome, where the city officials exercise a much more rigid control, though here, I am told, the problem for the professors is not so much the difficulty of preserving some sort of order and method in their classes as in collecting fees from students who are either unable or unwilling to pay. However, whatever the disadvantages in this respect, there is certainly more scope for a brilliant teacher and an accomplished scholar like Augustine in Rome than in Carthage. Indeed we have always expected him to go to Rome and he has often spoken of it himself. Up to now, I imagine, he has been deterred by his mother, who is reluctant to leave Africa herself and who, in spite of her not very well dissembled dislike of Lucilla and her strong disapproval of Augustine's friendship with the Manichees, cannot bear to be long separated from her favourite son.

It seems to me that now she will be more determined to cling to him than ever, since, according to Nebridius, he is rapidly losing all confidence in the Manichaean doctrines which he and I once found (or so we thought) so enlightening and inspiring. Nebridius tells me that the great Manichaean preacher Faustus is now in Carthage. He is enormously popular and it seems impossible to find a lecture hall big enough to accommodate all those who want to hear him speak.

According to Nebridius, his reputation is, at least in part, deserved. Augustine, and even Nebridius himself, were at first fascinated by his eloquence, his charm, his delightful choice of words and his ability to range from one subject to another, illuminating each one of them with ease and grace. He appears to have a great knowledge of literature and he speaks verse with such feeling and richness that even the best-known passages are heard as though for the first time. And all this learning and eloquence is devoted to the explication of the Manichaean doctrines and to exhortations to his hearers to adopt a way of life which he claims is true to the nature of things, colourful and, in the last resort, easy. However, it is just this question of the rationality of the creed which is now troubling Augustine and which, for a long time, has troubled Nebridius. In particular it seems to Augustine that the conclusions reached by Greek astronomers and mathematicians by means of measurement, observation and calculation provide a more rational explanation of the movements of the heavenly bodies than do the 'revelations' of Mani which, though they certainly introduce a spiritual element (for which Augustine is always looking) into the processes of nature, do not appear to conform to the facts of experiment and observation. For some time, I know, Augustine has been questioning leaders of the Manichees in Carthage on these points, and not unnaturally, since they lack his knowledge of mathematics and astronomy, they have been unable to satisfy his doubts. Recently, so Nebridius tells me, they have been simply telling him to wait until he can see Faustus and promising that then all will be explained.

This, however, has not come about. Nebridius says that Augustine was perfectly prepared to believe that the Manichees might be capable of producing an explanation of eclipses and other heavenly phenomena which fit in with their own doctrine and at the same time conform to the rational and certain conclusions of the Greeks. He sought and obtained an interview with Faustus just with this end in view—to be enlightened as to how the general world view of the Manichees could be held without contradicting the necessary conclusions of mathematics. He was profoundly disappointed. Faustus listened to him with great courtesy, but, so Nebridius writes, it soon became evident from the very expression of his face that he was quite incapable of following the argument which Augustine set before him and, not unwisely from the point of view of his own reputation, he made in the end no attempt to answer it. Instead he delighted all who were standing by by going off into a long disquisition on the subjects of beauty, of fitness, of similarities and dissimilarities, of inner and outer worlds, enlivening and illustrating his discourse with remarkably well-chosen passages from literature and philosophy. In the course of his speech he modestly disclaimed any great knowledge of astronomy and mathematics, and with the greatest politeness, somehow suggested that this knowledge was perhaps unnecessary and certainly of a lower order than that demanded for the development of his own themes.

Augustine was, as I can imagine, profoundly disheartened. He is an utterly generous man and he admired Faustus for his eloquence and charm, for which he certainly has a great reputation. He admired him too for not attempting to claim knowledge of subjects about which he was plainly ignorant; and indeed this is a rare quality to find anywhere, and in particular amongst those who profess to be scholars. But his disappointment was extreme. If the great Faustus could not answer his questions, then it was hopeless to look for any answer among the Manichees. And what, no doubt, depressed him most of all was the realization that the Manichees were not only incapable of answering him, but were not even interested in or able to grasp the relevance of the questions he asked. He has long been accustomed to regarding the Christians as even more prone to superstition and irrationality than the Manichees, and now, according to Nebridius, he is beginning to wonder whether after all the Epicureans are right. They do at least hold beliefs which are logically coherent and which are perfectly consistent with the findings of science and the impressions of sense. But I know that he cannot rest happily in these beliefs any more than I could. There is a frigidity about them which may serve, I suppose, as a kind of anaesthetic. The great spectacle or imagination of the eternal confluence of atoms has a certain grandeur and it seems to have imparted to some tortured minds, like that of the poet Lucretius, a sense of peace and security. But it is not the peace and security for which Augustine is looking. It is not relaxation that he seeks, but satisfaction.

Knowing him as I do, I am sorry for him in what must be his present state of mind. Yet I cannot help feeling glad that his dissatisfaction with Carthage may be bringing him to Rome, for he seems to me, as the poet says, a half of my own self.

IX

Yesterday, early in the morning, I was beginning to write a letter to Nebridius, but I was interrupted, and now I shall have much more to tell him. Indeed for me yesterday was a very eventful day. When my landlord came hurrying into my room I guessed from his excitement that I had received another message from Praetextatus, and this turned out to be the case. He invited me to dinner that evening and informed me that among the guests would be Symmachus, whom he described as an old acquaintance of mine. Of course I scarcely know Symmachus at all, having only met him once when he was pro-consul of Africa, but it was like Praetextatus to try to make me feel at ease in a society much more wealthy and influential than any which I have known. Symmachus has the reputation of being the greatest orator of the day. He has already held many important positions in the state and is soon to take up his duties as prefect of the city. I could not resist telling my landlord, who was standing impatiently by me as I read the letter, that I should be meeting Symmachus, because I wondered what his reactions to this news would be. For my landlord, having changed his religion at least once, now claims to be a Christian and takes as much interest in theological disputation as others do in chariot races, while Symmachus is the acknowledged spokesman of that majority of the nobility who worship, in one way or another, the old Gods. I had just finished reading a speech of his, recently published, in which he protested to the Emperor Gratian against the removal from the senate-house of the ancient statue of Victory which had been placed there more than four hundred years ago by the Emperor Augustus after the battle of Actium and to which all the senators, when taking their seats, used to burn a grain of incense. I had admired the speech both stylistically and because of the clever use made of appeals to the depths of sentiment which are implied by tradition and cannot be lightly disturbed. However, his main arguments had seemed rather unconvincing, since, if the state is supposed to be Christian, it is difficult to see how it can approve of sacrifices made to a pagan deity by public officials in a public capacity. In any case the Bishop of Milan, also a fine orator, spoke vigorously against Symmachus and his appeal was rejected.

The Christian community is, naturally enough, opposed to Symmachus, but, as I might have imagined, my landlord showed none of the theological hatred which, had a tenant of his not been invited to meet so great a man, he undoubtedly would have displayed. And as Praetextatus will soon take up the even more important office of praetorian prefect, his pride and satisfaction were all the greater. I wonder whether he will offer me an even better room.

But there was more in Praetextatus' letter to please me than an invitation, which was indeed a generous one to a person of my age and obscurity. In a postscript he wrote: 'If, as I hope, you will be able to come, we shall be able, I think, to celebrate some good news. I hear that you are to be offered a post as assessor to the count of the Italian treasury—a minor post, certainly, but a useful first step in your career.'

Of course I realized that I should owe this post to Praetextatus himself and I felt doubly grateful to him, not only for his having bothered to exert his influence on my behalf, but also because I knew that he would not exert his influence at all unless he had some confidence in my ability and integrity. Later in the day I received an official notification of my appointment. I am to take up my duties in a week's time.

I was surprised to find myself viewing this prospect with rather mixed feelings. I know that the appointment will please my parents, who have always encouraged me to make a success of the law and who no doubt have further ambitions for me. And I came to Rome in the first place just to seek some such a post as this. As Praetextatus says, it can lead to positions of more importance and I think that I am well qualified to do the work that will be required of me. I know too that this legal work, corrupt as it often is, is necessary to the very existence of an ordered society and, if I can avoid being corrupted (and I have neither the need nor the inclination to take bribes), it may be said that I am likely to do valuable work. Yet still I have an uneasy feeling that this is not really what I want to do with my life. It seems to me that I was more myself in the days when Augustine, Nebridius and I were pledging ourselves to the pursuit of wisdom. Yet I must own that even then we were not perfectly happy. We were, and are, confused. Even Augustine, it seems, has now lost whatever peace and security he found in the Manichaean view of life, and he too has a career in which he is being extremely successful. May it not be, too, that we can be aided, rather than hampered, in the search for wisdom by taking some part in the complexities of ordinary life and in gaining experience of the passions and behaviour of man as well as of the theoretical structures of philosophy and of the assurances, well or ill founded, of the various religious faiths? When I think, for instance, of Praetextatus, who is not only a scholar and a devoutly religious man, but has also held the highest offices in the state, I recognize a person with a greater depth and strength of character than my own and I feel ashamed to challenge or to dismiss beliefs of his which, in themselves, seem to me unsound or even pernicious. And so I am attempting to think more of my parents' pleasure when they hear of my appointment and of my own evident need for more experience of life than of that uneasiness at the back of my mind which makes me suspect that I am setting my life upon the wrong course.

In the evening I went to Praetextatus' house and, as I seem often to do, arrived, to my embarrassment, before any of the other guests. Praetextatus, however, soon put me at my ease. He questioned me about my new appointment and made light of my expressions of gratitude for the part which I knew he must have played in securing it for me. 'You have an excellent record on your own,' he told me, 'so that a word from me was hardly necessary.'

Soon Paulina entered the room and welcomed me with all the kindness which she had shown during my previous visit. Other guests too began to arrive. I knew none of them, except for Symmachus who, I should imagine, could hardly remember me, though he inquired after my parents and other families in our neighbourhood. I was glad to find myself during this part of the evening still in conversation with Paulina. I had mentioned to her that, since our last meeting, I had actually encountered the monk Jerome and also some of the ladies over whom, as she had told me, he exercised such a great and unfortunate influence. She was quick to ask me what my impressions were and I attempted to explain how mixed my feelings were with regard to the man. (How I wish that my feelings were not so often mixed!) He had spoken, I told her, with an arrogance, an intolerance and a lack of all good breeding which went beyond anything I had ever witnessed. And yet I had seen in him too an evident sincerity, a strange gentleness and even a kind of compassion which must demand respect and even sympathy. To this Paulina nodded her head gravely. 'I have heard,' she said, 'that he is demonic, and certainly my husband admires his scholarship. But I cannot believe in his sensitiveness, and I think that the spirits by which he is possessed are evil spirits. I say this because he seems to take pleasure in the sufferings and the deprivations of others. I hear, for instance, that that girl Blaesilla, whom you no doubt saw, now refuses to take any nourishment at all and is, in fact, dying of inanition. Jerome, it seems, actually approves of this conduct and encourages her austerities, promising her all kinds of satisfaction in another world, while he himself is content to stay in this one. Is this what you would expect in a man whom you call gentle and in whom you say that you have noticed signs of compassion?'

The question, framed as it was, was difficult to answer, though still I felt that Paulina, who had not seen Jerome as I had, was taking too easy and obvious a view of a situation which was more complex than she imagined. While I was searching for words, Symmachus, who had been listening to the latter part of our conversation, broke in upon it. While he was speaking I had an opportunity of observing him more closely than I had before.

He is a smallish man, with extremely intelligent eyes and a nose that is rather too long and sharp. While he speaks, and even in a private conversation, he uses his hands like a trained orator, but his gestures have a remarkable delicacy and, if they are employed rather too much, are certainly employed skilfully. His words are carefully chosen and his arguments are developed as they might be in a law court. He will give the impression that he is deeply and even modestly impressed by views which are, or can be imagined to be, opposed to his own, will then ridicule them or demolish them and conclude on a note of a too evident satisfaction with himself and with his own powers of expression. These are certainly remarkable, but are marred, to my mind, by his self-conceit and by a delight in the uses of language rather than in a candid examination of what is true or false. That he has convictions I do not doubt, but I suspect that these are rather a necessary background for the role that he has chosen to play than an integral part of his life and nature, as they are with Praetextatus or, for that matter, with Jerome. Long ago I had met a young man who was secretary to Symmachus in Africa. He told me that he was the vainest person he had ever known. He would write great numbers of letters and would have several copies made even of the least important of them. The letters were, of course, designed for eventual publication and the copies would constantly be altered and sometimes almost entirely rewritten. Indeed sentences and paragraphs would be inserted years after the writing of the original letter so as to indicate that Symmachus had possessed a greater prescience of the times than in fact had been the case. I thought of all this while I was listening to him now, and though I can recall roughly the sense of what he was saying, I cannot remember precisely the words he used or reproduce the exact balance of his phrases, the careful modulations of his cadences, let alone the slow or rapid gestures of arms or head—things which with part of my mind I admired and with part I found distasteful. As I listened I could not help contrasting his performance with what I remembered of Augustine. For Augustine can speak on a set theme with just as much grace and skill as Symmachus and, I should say, with a kind of originality which will distinguish his words even when he is speaking on the most hackneyed subjects and most closely following the rules of rhetoric. But in private conversations he is nothing but frank and open, will admit ignorance when he finds himself ignorant and, though he may often use rhetorical devices, which have now become to him part of his natural means of expression, would never dream of using them as a means of display with which to impress his friends. I should be inclined to doubt whether Symmachus has any friends.

'I believe,' he was saying, 'that I may be able to throw some light on the question which appears to be puzzling our young friend. On the one hand he sees, indeed we all see, instances of an inhumanity which must be condemned by custom and indeed by law. (The distinction between law and custom may indeed be made, but here, I think, is out of place.) We will agree that it is both unnatural and wrong for a young woman voluntarily, or under the influence of others, to deprive herself of the pleasures or forgo the duties of wife and mother. Particularly is this true of one like Blaesilla whose family goes back to the earliest days of the republic and in whose veins, it is said (though perhaps fancifully), runs the blood of the Gods themselves. It would appear, too, that this unfortunate young woman is actually seeking, by means of continual fasting and deprivation, to admit death rather than life; and what, indeed, is her dying life other than a living death? Such an impulse also conflicts with custom, law, religion and those deepest instincts which are their source. Life is the gift of the Gods and only under the most exceptional circumstances may this gift be voluntarily surrendered. Examples of such circumstances will occur to you all. Let me only mention Decius Mus and, as I think I may do in a circle of such distinguished friends, Cato of Utica.' Here he paused, as though waiting for applause for his boldness in bringing forward the name of a man who had undeviatingly (and, to my mind, rather stupidly) opposed the first Caesar, the 'divine Julius', as he is still called, in the cause of the senate and the constitution. As this name, though no doubt seldom spoken in front of the emperor himself, has always been revered among the senatorial nobility, no boldness whatever was required in bringing it forward in the presence of

Praetextatus and his friends. However, it was greeted with a reverent silence. Symmachus had made his point. He now continued, first indicating me with a rapid gesture, as though to show that I had been privileged to serve him as a starting-point for the theme which he was developing. 'But on the other hand,' he said, 'this young man can see (and this does him much credit) at least the appearance of a kind of virtue in this self-inflicted suffering of Blaesilla, suffering which, as we have agreed, may end in suicide. It is in the name of religion that she is depriving herself not only of the company of men, but of that material sustenance which preserves and nourishes the life of man and woman alike. At this point each one of you, I am sure, is thinking of the relevant passage in Lucretius.' Here again he paused and took in the whole circle of his audience with a swish of his hand. In fact the famous line 'To so much evil has religion led the way' had never even crossed my mind, nor do I think it had occurred to anyone else. But Symmachus had, or thought he had, made his effect by this rather laboured flattery of our presumed knowledge of literature. It seemed to me a poor form of flattery since everyone who has read anything at all is perfectly familiar with the pathetic passage describing the sacrifice of Iphigeneia at Aulis. Others, perhaps, may have felt as I did, for Symmachus immediately went on. 'I shall not press the relevance of those lines and one of my reasons for not doing so is that the description of Iphigeneia in Lucretius is derived from Aeschylus who uses the same incident for a quite different purpose than that of our Roman poet.' Here he paused again as though reluctant to abandon an interesting disquisition on literary criticism. And indeed his views on this point would have interested me more than his present elucidation of what were supposed to be my ideas but were in fact ideas attributed to me by him. He turned to me again and began to address me with a certain asperity in his voice. I knew, of course, that he had no ill feelings towards me and did not even regard me as being particularly stupid; but I had somehow been chosen to be the defendant in a case where he would be able to display his talents. 'If,' he went on, 'this young man would follow logically the proposition which he is defending, he would have to condone the excesses of such people as the Galli, who castrate themselves in the honour of of their Goddess (a practice which, I believe, is also recommended by some of the Christians); but the experience of our ancestors, the wisdom of Rome, has decided to penalize any Roman citizen who, whether his motives are sincere or not, chooses to deprive his country and himself of the full exercise of his manhood. We take this view with regard to even the humblest and most worthless of our citizens. How much more must we deplore the decision of a young and virtuous lady coming, as I have said, from one of the greatest families, to take what is, if we allow for the difference of sex, just the same course as one of these Phrygian priests? Certainly, I say, let us respect religion and all admonitions from the Gods, but let us remember that of all the signs from heaven there is, as Homer says, one and one only that is the best, and that is to do one's duty to one's country.'

Here he again eyed me severely. Then, since he had reached what he regarded as a satisfactory conclusion, his expression changed to one of benevolence and he touched me lightly on the shoulder, almost as though he were congratulating me on having performed my part well, or as if all that remained for me to do was to express my gratitude to him for his enlightenment and his forbearance. I myself was annoyed. My ideas, such as they were, had been wholly misrepresented. I had had no intention of commending self-inflicted castration and was about to say so when it occurred to me that whatever I said would only lead to another set speech from Symmachus. I noticed that Praetextatus was looking slightly amused. He probably understood my feelings and sympathized with me. Probably, too, he had noticed, as I had done, the inappropriateness of Symmachus' quotation from Homer, which, in any case, he had translated incorrectly. It is a remark made by Hector to justify the only stupid military decision he makes in the course of the Iliad. I was disgusted to observe how pleased with himself Symmachus was after his display. He now behaved to me with the greatest cordiality and, among other things, asked me who were the best-known young professors of rhetoric in Carthage. I mentioned the name of Augustine and Symmachus nodded his head approvingly. He had heard, he said, of that young man and would strongly advise him to come to Rome, where there were better prospects than in Carthage. I told him that Augustine was very likely to come to Rome quite soon and Symmachus expressed interest, before turning with some avidity to the food and drink set before him. Wishing to be of some service to my friend, I spoke all the more warmly of Augustine, overcoming, as I did so, the distaste I felt for Symmachus himself. He listened, I should guess, to about half of what I said.

Nor, I am glad to say, did he speak again at any great length that evening. This, I fancy, was partly because of his excellent appetite, which he was indulging freely, and partly because he was as ignorant as I was of the military matters which were being discussed. In any case he contented himself with a number of learned and more or less apposite quotations and various moral reflections unexceptional in their tenor and expressed with considerable verbal felicity. I myself listened intently to the conversation both because of its political importance and also so that I should have much more up-to-date information to send on to Nebridius.

Not only Praetextatus himself but several of his guests had been or were military officers of high rank. Much of their discussion concerned the strength or weakness of various fortresses, the practicability of this or that route through the mountains of Gaul or the Alps and other subjects of which I knew little or nothing. But I could understand why these were naturally the topics of their conversation. They had had much more recent news from the West than had reached me or the ordinary citizen of Rome. It was known to them that Maximus, commander of the armies in Britain, had actually landed in Gaul and had been already joined by large contingents of the Emperor Gratian's army. One of the guests, an elderly man who had held high commands under Gratian in his early youth and at the time of his victories, spoke with deep emotion of what had happened and what was likely to happen. None of the others showed any affection for Gratian at all. Some, I gathered, had been alienated from him by what they regarded as his persecution of the old religion of the Romans; all were offended by his treatment of the army, his ridiculous affectation of foreign dress and manners, his neglect of the frontiers and his decline from a life of discipline and honour to one of pure self-indulgence. No one seemed to think that he had the remotest chance of holding Gaul. His only hope, they agreed, was either to make his way to Constantinople and beg for the support of Theodosius, who certainly had reason to be grateful to him and who had sufficient force to back him, or else to retire at once to Italy and then act in conjunction with his fellow-emperor and half-brother, the boy Valentinian II. There was general agreement that the passes over the Alps could be held, so long as there was no defection from the armies in Italy, but it was also agreed that they would be more efficiently held by the generals of young Valentinian than under the command of Gratian himself.

There was something about this conversation, clear and lucid as it was, which I found disturbing. Perhaps it was its very abstraction. For no one, except one elderly general, appeared to be at all interested in the fate of Gratian himself. It was not that these people were indifferent to what was happening. They were all patriots and most of them came from the highest circles in the Roman aristocracy. The name and fortunes of Rome meant more to them, I should say, than to me who, though I am proud to be a Roman and though all my thought and feeling has been shaped by Roman tradition,

still regard Africa as my country. I feel no particular deference towards the Roman senate which, in fact, has exercised
no substantial power for the last four hundred years, and I
had been unable to understand the indignation expressed so
eloquently by Symmachus at the mere removal from the
senate-house of an ancient statue which was, in any case,
Greek in origin. None the less this indignation, unjustified
though it seemed to me, was certainly a mark of a deep and
sincere feeling for tradition, for order and for the notion of
stability which is associated with the name of Rome. Yet now
when, for all they knew, an emperor was fleeing for his life or
might even have already lost it, no one seemed to regard the
event as either deplorable or pitiable. They were concerned
either with the immediate military prospects or with the
possibilities of another emperor showing a more decent consideration for the ancient religion. It occurred to me that,
able and practical men as many of the senatorial nobility still
are, their deepest interest is not in the present, but in the past,
state of Rome. They are proud not of their own achievements
so much as of those of their ancestors, and they will speak of
the ancient republic, of which nearly all traces have long
disappeared, almost as though it is still in existence. Is it that
they too, like myself and my friends, are in fact bewildered
by the world in which they live? It is true that they find a
security and basis for their lives in conventions and beliefs
which I and my friends tend to regard with scepticism, indifference or contempt. They are indeed more satisfied with
themselves and their surroundings than we are. But so is a
drunkard, and so are those elders of the Manichees to whom
Augustine and I used to listen with such respect. Yet their
satisfaction, resting as it is on a kind of dream, is not the
happiness that we seek. So it seemed to me that these men's
almost devout belief in the idea of Rome might not be very
much more respectable than a drunkard's adoration of the
bottle or the enjoyment of a Manichee in an explanation of the
world that conflicted with the findings of science. For the

reality of Rome was something different from their idea of it.

This impression of mine—the impression of talented and able people believing themselves to be living in a world that no longer existed—was strengthened by the final events of the evening. A servant had summoned Praetextatus from the room and after a little while he returned, carrying a letter which he had evidently just received. One could see from his expression that it contained news of importance. He read it to us clearly and calmly. It was a dispatch from Milan telling of the treacherous assassination of the Emperor Gratian, who, after having been deserted by his troops, had entrusted himself to a provincial governor on whom he thought he could rely. He had been handed over to Maximus' general of cavalry and immediately put to death. The young Valentinian, or rather, it would seem, the Bishop of Milan, had demanded the body of the dead emperor in order to give it proper burial, but this request had been refused. Now all Gaul, Britain and Spain were in the hands of Maximus.

I noticed that, as Praetextatus read the letter, people avoided looking at each other. The old general who had known Gratian well was the only one present to show signs of pity or indignation at the news which we were hearing. The rest adopted non-committal expressions, though in the face of Symmachus there appeared something very like satisfaction. For a few moments no one said anything until Symmachus remarked: 'At least no Roman blood has been shed.'

Praetextatus looked at him gravely. 'If we exclude', he said, 'that of the Emperor himself.'

This rebuke (for it was clearly intended as such) embarrassed Symmachus and he began at some length unnecessarily to explain himself. No one paid much attention to him and no one seemed anxious to express an opinion of his own. I fancied that only Praetextatus, to whom they were all looking for some sort of guidance, was deeply shocked not so much, perhaps, by the death of Gratian as by the illegitimacy and brutality of the revolution that had taken place. He may well have been reflecting, as I was, that this was nothing new in the history of Rome. Emperor after emperor has seized rather than succeeded to power. The 'Roman people', as it is still called in official documents, has long ceased to exist as a political force; the senate indeed has continued to provide magistrates, generals and administrators and, as a body, it has sometimes for long periods been treated with some respect; but no one except for a few senators themselves could regard it as ever having exercised a decisive influence on affairs since the last days of the republic. The fact, seldom openly admitted, but perfectly clear to see, was that in the last resort power depended on the ability to use armed force. That this power was to be used in the interests of justice, morality and religion was a claim that had nearly always been made and there is always, even among savages, some vague and general idea as to what these interests are. In practice, however, these words have been appropriated, with various degrees of cynicism or sincerity, by the ambition of generals, the greed of armies, the indolence of the poor or the self-interest of the rich. It seems to me that behind this still brilliant façade of empire—the state processions, the display of church dignitaries, the shows, the almost oriental ceremony of the court—there lies something more like despair than hope. Perhaps so many people, including Praetextatus himself, would not be so interested in securing their interests in a life after death if they had not reason to suppose that in this life, and in this political organization, justice was unreliable, security unlikely and certainty impossible.

I do not know whether these ideas or any like them were passing through the mind of Praetextatus. Certainly his powerful face showed distress and I fancy that this distress was increased by the evident irresolution or vacuity of mind to be observed in most of his guests. He merely remarked, 'Our allegiance is, of course, due to the Emperor Valentinian and Theodosius.' The others waited for him to proceed, but he rose from the table, putting an end to further discussion and the guests dispersed rapidly and, I thought, rather shame-facedly. They were too obviously thinking first of all of their own interests and speculating in what direction it would be most safe or profitable to move. What impressed me was their utter powerlessness.

X

This morning I went to call on the judge who presides over the court to which I am to be attached. I found him polite, but rather over-anxious to impress me with his knowledge of the law. He told me that we should soon have before us a very difficult case in which a leading senator was involved. It appeared to me, from his brief summary, that the case was far from difficult; this senator was merely making a wholly un-justifiable claim against the treasury. When I said so, the judge appeared momentarily embarrassed and then went on to speak, very kindly, of my lack of experience and of the distinction, which can only be made by men of long experience in such cases, between a general equity and a particular application of the precise provisions of justice. He closed on a somewhat jovial and literary note, saying, as though the idea had only just occurred to him, that this particular senator had great power in city affairs and was able, like Medea in the play of Euripides, 'to hurt his enemies and help his friends'. He then immediately changed the subject and began to ask my opinion of the abilities of various leading lawyers in Carthage. I was somewhat offended by his frequent use of the word 'provincial' and by his recurring comment, 'We do things differently in Rome.' In fact he is very like many of the lawyers whom I have met in Africa, being vain, opinionated and, I suspect, timid.

After this interview was over I wrote a long letter to Nebridius. I could now add to my previous information an account of how the news of the emperor's assassination had been received in Rome. It had been received with almost complete indifference. Indeed it seems to me that, if the word 'provincial' can be applied to anybody, it would be most properly applied to the Romans themselves. There are frequent military engagements on the frontiers of the empire but the people of Rome are indifferent to them. They are not alarmed by news of defeat and only take notice of a victory on those rare occasions when some emperor sends them barbarian captives to be slaughtered in the arena. Even the courts of Milan or Trèves appear to them remote and scarcely connected with their own life. As for Constantinople, the only interest it excites is among that large proportion of the Christian community which is anxiously concerned with the progress or decline of various heresies. Any idea that Italy or Rome itself could be invaded and overrun by a hostile army would be dismissed as incredible.

Nebridius himself has often spoken with contempt of this false security, but in Africa I myself was more impressed at the time by the strength of his feelings than by the truth of what he was saying. Since I have been in Rome I can see that he was indeed speaking the truth.

Indeed there have been many occasions when Nebridius, with his hard good sense and his careful examination of facts, has helped me and Augustine too, though Augustine, as Nebridius would readily agree, has a mind more brilliant, forcible and subtle than ours. At the time when Augustine was seriously interested in astrology (and he would still like to see, if he could, that kind of perfect correspondence between the greater and lesser parts of the universe which astrologers claim as the basis for their science) it was Nebridius who most energetically and effectively argued against him. And though Nebridius as well as I was for some time a Manichaean, he was much more sceptical than I was on the subject. He was more impressed by the destructive criticism of the Manichees than by their positive doctrines. He never bothered to examine this doctrine with the thoroughness of Augustine, and perhaps he was wise here. I myself followed Augustine closely, as indeed I always do. I remember how at that time Augustine often used to take me to the houses of those Manichaeans who are far advanced in the gnosis and who are called 'the Elect'. We would bring vegetables and fruit for them which we had picked or cut ourselves, since one of the Elect will not so much as pick a fig from the tree with his own hand, believing, as he does, that the fig suffers from the act and that it would be wrong for him to risk a diminution in his own purity by causing that suffering. I was not impressed by this argument, since it seemed to me that the man who in the end eats the fig is at least indirectly responsible for whatever suffering may be caused in the picking of it. But Augustine explained that a distinction must be made between the doing of the act and its final result. The picking of the fig, since it caused pain, was in itself bad and the badness of the act would have a worse effect on a superior soul, like that of one of the Elect, than it would have on less advanced consciousnesses such as his and mine. Yet the final result was wholly good, since it was believed that the fig, by incorporation into the body of one of the Elect, would enjoy its own form of liberation. In the process of digestion, by exhalation or by other means, those particles of light that had subsisted, as it were buried, in the fruit, would be freed from darkness and, joining the pure air, would increase the sum total of redeemed and transformed matter. Thus it was a common saying among the Elect that, after their vegetarian meals, they were 'breathing out angels'. I own that I was not wholly satisfied with this explanation, and I doubt whether Augustine was either. But his intellect is at the same time more powerful and more ardent than mine. Nebridius says of him that he wants to believe more than he can and, in a sense, this is true, though he will never hold a view which in the end, and after full investigation, he discovers to be false.

Certainly at that time we were both, we thought, followers of these doctrines. Many of the Manichaeans whom we met were cultured men, or at least they appeared to us to be so. They were confident in their beliefs, but much more tolerant of the beliefs of others than are the Christians. Around the Elect, it is true, there was often an atmosphere of some austerity and even sanctity, though even among the Elect one will find men with the most genial and expressive manners. Some are very brilliant conversationalists and they take pleasure in exposing and joking about what are to them the evident absurdities and crudities of Christian belief—the notion, for instance, that a God who is all spirit can possibly have been subjected to the physical processes of birth from a woman's body, whether or not the conception itself was miraculous.

Augustine, who has not only the keenest of intelligences, but also a fine wit and a great sense of enjoyment, often took a leading part in these conversations and would delight me and Nebridius and other friends with his subtle and amusing analyses of the evident contradictions which seem to be accepted quite happily by the Christians. He was, of course, more careful in speaking with his mother, who is a very pious Christian herself and who has an almost extravagant affection for him. I say 'extravagant' not because he does not deserve her love, but because it sometimes seems to me that she seems scarcely to notice her other children when he is in the room. Augustine is certainly much more talented than his brother and sister, both of whom are pleasant enough people, devout Christians themselves and very fond of Monnica. Perhaps Monnica thinks that they are both, as the Christians say, 'saved' already, and that there is therefore no reason why she should give them particular attention. But I think it is more than this. Both she and Patricius made great sacrifices for the sake of Augustine's education and I think that she, in her own way, just as Patricius did in his, feels that for this investment she is entitled to a suitable return. Patricius wanted Augustine to be a success in his profession, which indeed he is, and, in expansive moments, would speak of how some professors of rhetoric have reached the highest possible positions in the state—governors of provinces, consuls, advisers to the emperor. Monnica would pretend to agree with him as, I had noticed, she often used to do, since this avoided quarrels and also, as was often shown, made it easy for her, in fact, always in the end to get her own way. But she had something else in mind too. She wants him to become a great and distinguished man by being able to develop all the talents which he possesses, but she hopes or imagines that in the end these talents will be devoted to the service of her religion. She would rather see him bishop of Rome or Milan than a consul or a senator. And so her attention is constantly upon him and her affection seems concentrated on him rather to the exclusion of her other two children. They, I must say, do not appear to resent it. The girl, who is very devout herself, perhaps shares her mother's feelings. Certainly, like her mother, she dislikes Lucilla, though they are both fond of the little child. As for the brother, he takes in many ways after Patricius though, in spite of his better manners, I do not find him so attractive. He, like his father, without being highly educated, respects education in others, admiring them either for their prospects or for the salary or public position which they attain. But Patricius, bad-tempered and impulsive as he often was, had a kind of natural force and charm about him which Augustine's brother does not share. In fact there is more of these qualities in Augustine himself. He wants to excel and he wants to love and be loved. His brother, I think, is not ambitious and wants only to be respected. He is less offended by his mother's evidently preferring Augustine to himself in her affection than by her habit of always consulting

Augustine first in practical matters, such as farming, about which he is not particularly well informed.

Like most people whose affections are concentrated on one object, Monnica is exceedingly jealous. She is not jealous of Nebridius, me and a few others of Augustine's friends, possibly because she sees that he has a greater influence on us than we have on him. But she is very jealous of Lucilla and is, I think, often unkind to her. Not that Lucilla has any influence over Augustine intellectually nor in any case could Monnica charge her with encouraging him in anti-Christian views. She is herself a Christian, but of a simple, devout kind, quite uninterested in any questions of theology. I do not think that she is at all concerned with Augustine's beliefs, since her attachment to him is not of a kind which could make her ever want to control his mind. She admires him for being cleverer than she is, loves him at least as passionately as does Monnica and asks nothing of him except the enjoyment of the pleasures and the warmth of feeling which they share together. Augustine once told me that he first met her in a church in Carthage to which he had followed her because he was attracted by her manner and appearance. This must have been ten or twelve years ago, since he was a student at the time. In those days, he tells me, he was always looking for love affairs and always finding in them more pain than pleasure. If his advances were rejected, he would fall into a misery of self-reproach, imagining that his failure to make himself loved must spring from some fault or blemish in his own nature of which he was ignorant and of which he ought to be aware. And when he was successful, he was still unhappy when not actually in the presence of his lover. When away from her, he would be tortured by jealousy, and this was not because he was, in the ordinary sense of the word, unduly possessive, but rather because he looked in vain for a completeness of mutual confidence which is rarely to be found except in friendship and for a kind of totality of surrender of which he himself was capable but which most others, for one reason or another, fear and avoid. But with Lucilla he seemed to find what he was looking for. This love affair was passionate from the beginning. I am inclined to fancy that the very fact that it originated and was, for a short time, carried on in a church (something that would have horrified his mother) helped to fix his heart in the direction it had found. He imagined, I think, that there was some proof of the strength and sincerity of her affection for him in her being able to commit such an act of sacrilege and he loved her the more for the sacrifice which it seemed to him that she was making. In fact, I should say, Lucilla, though her affection is as strong and sincere as he could wish, was simple and innocent enough not to feel any sense of sin in what she was doing. She loves whole-heartedly and cannot see, as the Manichaeans tell us that we should see, that the physical expression of her love, whether it results in child-bearing or not, is anything but natural and good. She does not reflect upon the nature of the body and the soul, their interaction or opposition, as Augustine and I do. She would be indifferent, I think, to the kind of intellectual or philosophical excitement which, I imagine, Praetextatus and his wife find in the act of sex, and she would certainly fail to understand what Jerome means by the uncleanness of it or by the rapture which he feels in contemplation of the state of virginity. It seems to me that this simplicity of hers, with its own strange purity, is the quality in her which most binds Augustine to her. Since he began to live with her he has never followed another woman, nor would she dream of being associated with another man. This is certainly the kind of fidelity which poets have longed for, though seldom found, and which is also commended by some philosophers and religious men. I myself, though I am afraid of women, still with some part of me wish that I could feel, with no kind of afterthought or reservation, that innocent, vivid and resignedly confident fervour which I see in her. For even I, for a short moment, have experienced something of the same kind.

Augustine told me once that at the beginning they were so absorbed in the newness and ecstasy of their enjoyment that they were both amazed and startled when Lucilla, as was natural enough, became pregnant. It had not seemed to them that the bearing and bringing up of a child could be a consequence of, or indeed have any connection with the ardour of their love-making. Augustine owns that at first he was disappointed. Lucilla too, though happy and proud to be bearing his child, was also somewhat fearful that this very evidence of maternity and all the cares and distractions necessarily entailed by the presence of a child in their lives might somehow alienate his affection from her. But her fears proved quite groundless and as for him, as soon as the baby was born, he became as devoted to his son as she was. Indeed he showed a kind of extravagance of affection which we, his friends, found both touching and amusing. He had been in the habit often of talking of the sins, the inadequacies and the miseries of his own childhood and of that of others. But with regard to his own son, Adeodatus, he could find no fault at all. He will often belittle his own intelligence, but he looks with a proud amazement at every sign of intelligence that he discovers in Adeodatus. And here, though he may have shown initially only the partiality of a father, his feelings have certainly been justified by the event, for the little boy does have exceptional ability. Moreover he has a most sweet and winning disposition. He excels, as Augustine did in his schooldays, but he excels effortlessly, it seems, arouses no jealousy in his companions and is loved wherever he is. Augustine seems to believe him to be too good for this world and says that whenever he looks at him he thinks with terror of the old (and demonstrably untrue) saying that those whom the Gods love die young. He shows more agitation even than Lucilla or Monnica whenever the child is in the least ill and will go to great expense and trouble in securing medicines in which he has been persuaded to have faith and which are often, and probably rightly, rejected by the two women.

It was during the early childhood of Adeodatus that Monnica was persuaded to look less harshly on Lucilla than she did before or has done later. It seems often to happen that a mother will show jealousy of her daughter-in-law and Monnica, knowing as she does the depth of affection of which her son is capable, perhaps had more reason than most for fearing that her own influence might be superseded. But she is fond of children and was perhaps particularly glad to have a grandchild so soon after the death of her husband, Patricius. Also, of course, she knew much more than Lucilla did about the care of young children and so was able to take up once more that dominating position in the household which she used to have. Before the birth of the child she would be apt to call attention to Lucilla's humble origins and lack of any kind of property, even though her own birth was not very distinguished, and her own means not more than barely adequate. Augustine, indeed, would not have been able to finish his courses at Carthage, had it not been for the financial aid of our rich neighbour, Romanianus. Now, however, Monnica began to look more kindly on Lucilla. She would laugh at her for her ignorance and incompetence, natural enough in a young girl, and was glad to help her with her superior knowledge of everything to do with babies. It may be unjust of me to suppose that she would have been happier if Lucilla had remained incompetent and somewhat helpless, and if the very fact of child-bearing had made her to Augustine less an object of passion than before. In fact Lucilla has turned out to be a good mother and Augustine has remained passionately devoted to her. As these two facts became more and more evident, so the relations between the two women have deteriorated. Indeed there was a period when Monnica refused to sit at the same table with her son and daughter-in-law. Ostensibly the reason for this was that she was offended by Augustine's increasing involvement with the Manichees and the irreverence which he was apt to show towards various dogmas of the Catholic Church. Undoubtedly Monnica believed herself that this was the true reason for the action, but I have observed that people very often act from reasons which are more evident to others than to themselves, and in this case I am inclined to think that Monnica's severe behaviour towards a son whom she loved more than all else was in fact an effort to establish her own authority at the expense of Lucilla. She could scarcely maintain that Augustine's Manichaeism had anything to do with Lucilla, who continued to attend Catholic services regularly, but she could still find it possible to blame her for not showing sufficient distaste for his views and for being just as ready to welcome his love as ever. Augustine himself was deeply distressed by his mother's disapproval and, as always when he encounters any hostility from one he loves, was prepared to look for the fault in himself. He was careful to say nothing to offend her and would attempt to show his real affection by numbers of small acts of kindness. But it was not in his nature to do what his mother wished him to do. Would she have him, he asked her, pretend to believe what in his heart and to the best of his ability he found to be false? This was an argument which might satisfy a philosopher, but it left Monnica indifferent. Truth, she maintained, had already been revealed. It was known partially by her and it had been known and tested by men who were wiser and more experienced than her son. But these two positions are quite irreconcilable, so that, with no compromise possible, the quarrel seemed interminable. For, while mother and son were bound together by the deepest affection, intellectually each was as stubborn as the other. Both, I am sure, suffered greatly. Augustine has told me how his mother would spend hours every day in praying for him and in weeping for what seemed to her not only the certain ruin of all her hopes but actually his final damnation. Augustine himself, deprived not of his mother's affection but of the usual manifestations of it, was acutely unhappy. Sometimes, it seems, Monnica's own distress was alleviated by dreams or visions which, so she believed, declared to her that her tears would not be in vain and that there would come a time when her son would believe as she wished him to believe and to act as she wished him to act. She could see herself and him standing in the same place. No one else, and certainly not Lucilla, was ever visible in these dreams. But Augustine's very honesty would compel him to refuse to accept her interpretation of these dreams of hers, though they certainly made him uneasy enough. I think that at this period he turned to Lucilla with a passion that was somehow more desperate and, as I should say, less natural than before. Perhaps he was attempting to find satisfaction in her for emotions of different kinds, both the love of a man for his mistress and the mother of his child and also that love of his own mother of which he seemed to be deprived. As for Lucilla, it seemed to me that, while she was pleased and proud to find him so totally occupied with her, she was at the same time somehow alarmed by the intensity of it all, feeling perhaps that though she was well able to satisfy and to share in the emotions of a lover, she was less capable of fulfilling a role which was not hers or, if at all so, only so by accident.

It may be, I think, that in this painful situation it was Lucilla, finally, who was the most unfortunate, for nothing could ever break the bonds of affection between Augustine and Monnica, whereas she, torn between two such powerful natures, may have been unable perfectly to express her own nature from which too much was being demanded.

In the end the great love which always subsisted between mother and son proved too strong to be denied and there was some kind of a reconciliation. It was characteristic of the two that, basically, neither gave way an inch. Monnica received Augustine and Lucilla again at her table and Augustine was inexpressibly delighted with this and was more than ever careful to say nothing which could offend her. But she left him in no doubt that she continued every day to pray for him and to weep for what was to her his evident transgression from the truth. And when any subject of a religious nature came up for discussion between him and his friends, she would immediately leave the room. As for Augustine, he remained deeply disturbed by her distress for him, but he continued to follow and to inquire into the teachings of the Manichees, and in private conversation he would still ridicule the writings of the Christians for their lack of any style or refinement and their doctrines for logical incoherency. He was able, however, once again and for much of the time to show and to share the old warmth of feeling which persisted between himself and his mother. He was constantly commending her kindness and generosity to Lucilla who, on such a subject, could not venture to disagree with him. But I am sure that in her heart she feels differently. She is frightened of Monnica's kindness. Once she said to me, 'She is determined to get rid of me', and then, terrified of what she had said, made me promise not to pass on her words to Augustine. I tried to reassure her, since Monnica is indeed kind, but I could see that my assurances were not convincing her. Moreover, to tell the truth, I was not wholly convinced by them myself.

All this happened, of course, before I came to Rome and I do not know how this uneasy situation has developed. In his letters to me here Augustine always sends me the warmest greetings from both his mother and Lucilla, but most of what he writes is concerned with questions of philosophy or with the doings of our various friends. Now that he has become, according to Nebridius, almost wholly disillusioned with the teaching of the Manichees, he will at least gratify his mother in one respect. But what she really wants is for him to become a Christian and his objections to that faith are, I am sure, as strong as ever. However, I shall soon know all about this and how delighted I shall be to welcome him in Rome!

*part
two*

I

I have now been working for two weeks in the assessor's court and tomorrow the case with which we have been busy will be closed. But how can I think of that now, after the news which I have just received? Augustine is actually in Rome and I shall see him tomorrow evening. I have just been visited by the man in whose house he is staying and I would have gone immediately to see my friend if he had not told me that the doctor had left the strictest orders that Augustine must receive no visitors until tomorrow. I found that he had been extremely and dangerously ill, but is now considered to be quite out of danger, though he is still weak and only just beginning to take nourishment. I listened with dismay as this good man, Proculeius by name, told me that for several days they had almost given up hope of his recovery. Why, I asked Proculeius, had he not summoned me at once? I would have got for him the best doctors in Rome and my presence in itself might have been of some help and satisfaction to him. Proculeius told me that Lucilla, who is with him, had suggested this very thing, but that Augustine had forbidden her to get in touch with me until he was better. He knew, he had said, that his sickness would cause me pain and he wished to cause pain to as few people as possible. For the next few days he had been in a high fever, delirious and often incapable of recognizing even Lucilla or Adeodatus. I inquired about his mother and discovered that she had been left behind in Africa. This news surprised me; for though Monnica is deeply attached to Africa she is still more deeply attached to her son and so I found it difficult to believe that she had not wished to accompany him. Proculeius, too, encouraged me to think that there was something here which required explanation. It appears that during the height of his illness Augustine had constantly called for his mother by name and had seemed to be reproaching himself for some injury which he imagined that he had done to her. On this subject Lucilla had been unwilling to speak fully; she may well have been irritated by the fact that in his delirium her name had been seldom or never uttered. Indeed, so Proculeius tells me, the only name often repeated, apart from that of Monnica, was my own. This fact made me all the more distressed that I had not been informed of his illness earlier. However, I could not linger long over this disappointment, so great was my joy in knowing that he had made a complete recovery and that I was to see him tomorrow.

No doubt I should have plied Proculeius with questions for half the day if he had been able to afford the time. But he had other appointments in the city and so was only able to stay with me for about an hour. I found him a most agreeable man. He is a Manichaean, of whom there are great numbers in Rome, and told me that several leading members of the sect in Carthage had written to him about Augustine in the warmest terms. Even though Augustine fell ill so soon after his arrival, he has already seen enough of him to feel his charm and admire his abilities, though he owns that he is surprised and somewhat distressed to find in him a faith less fervent than his own. Soon after his arrival and before he became ill, Augustine told him that, in his view, many of the teachings of Mani are plainly indefensible. This remark, coming from one who had been so highly praised by his Manichaean friends in Carthage, had shocked Proculeius, though he had been somewhat relieved when Augustine had added that, in spite of his reservations with regard to much of the doctrine, he could find no satisfaction at all in any other faith. Could it be, Proculeius asked me, that Augustine's moment of scepticism might be caused merely by the onset of a serious illness? I explained that I regarded this as unlikely, but, since Proculeius is a pious man and I have no wish to hurt his feelings, I refrained from expressing my conviction that Augustine will never again become a wholehearted believer in his sect. He will never rest except in complete certainty and in a truth to which he can surrender himself entirely.

But Proculeius, unlike many of the Christians, is a tolerant man who respects learning and sincerity even when they are found outside the circle of his own religious beliefs. He is already fond of Augustine and is confident that he and his friends will be able to find students for him when he is able to set up his own school of rhetoric. Indeed he hopes that Augustine will make use of his house for this purpose, and he was pleased when I told him that of all the professors of rhetoric whom I have met, Augustine is incomparably the most able. He left me with the warmest expressions of goodwill, and I, for my part, can scarcely wait till tomorrow comes and think of the important decisions I shall have to make before then.

And indeed, so far as the decisions themselves are concerned no thought is in fact necessary, since they are already made. It is merely a question of the precise attitude I should adopt and the precise phrases which I should use when it is my turn to give my opinion. The case itself is perfectly plain. To grant the concessions which this rich and powerful senator demands would be in direct contravention of the law. Perhaps I am too naïve, but I must own that I am surprised to find that every member of the court except for me is perfectly prepared to do this. I imagine they have all been approached, as I have been, by agents of this senator who have promised certain advantages, in the form of either money or position, if the decision is given in his favour, and have hinted at disagreeable possibilities should it go the other way. Of course it does not surprise me that a man of his wealth and influence should use both of these in an effort to evert justice. This often happens. Great men have always been apt to think that the law is their servant. But the fact that bribery and intimidation are common does not make them less shocking. How, I wonder, would I have been able to face Augustine tomorrow if I had feared the threats or listened to the offers which have been made to me? Our friendship is grounded, certainly, in affection, but this affection would not be what it is if either of us thought the other capable of plain dishonesty. I was not, of course, in any way tempted or disturbed by the words of the senator's agents, and perhaps here I am luckier than some of my colleagues. For I should not mind if I did lose my post and, if I lost it in such a way as this, I could count on the approval of my parents. But most of my colleagues are poorer and older men than I am. They dread the prospect of unemployment and they would grasp eagerly at any opportunity for advancement. As for the president of the court, he is in a somewhat different position. He is well off financially and he has over the years built up for himself a high reputation as a lawyer. In his last interview with me he admitted (of course in confidence) that with regard to this case he entirely agrees with the stand which I have taken. He went on to explain by a most tortuous chain of argument that it was not his duty to declare his opinion openly, but rather to remain bound by the unanimous opinion of the courts. Were the opinion of the court anything other than unanimous, the senator's appeal would automatically be dismissed, but it would go on record that the only dissentient voice had been mine. It was, I think, rather kind of him to speak to me in this way. He was making it plain that if there is anything to fear from the senator's displeasure, I shall be the only one on whom this displeasure will fall and that he will do nothing openly to support me. But he is, I fancy, secretly pleased with my decision to continue to oppose the opinion of the others, since, if his court were to reach a verdict so flagrantly illegal as that proposed, he would lose some of the credit which he has acquired with the public and in his profession. He made it clear that he would be most gratified if I were to refrain from insisting openly that he should declare his own opinion.

My opposition in itself, he said, would be sufficient for the quashing of the case. Besides, he said, the duty of a president and indeed of any lawyer as eminent as himself was to act simply as a moderator, an interpreter of the law and not, if possible, to engage in the heat of controversy.

I still think it was kind of him to explain, however obscurely, that he proposed to desert his real duty and to leave all responsibility to me, and I doubt whether he imagined that I was taking seriously his involved and casuistical exposition designed to justify his own cowardice. Nevertheless I am saddened by the whole affair, even though I tell myself that I have long known that neither the law nor the practice of it are what they pretend to be. We are brought up to believe that the law is the most sacred of the institutions of civilization, the guardian of our liberties, the distillation of all the political and moral wisdom of the past. On this theme no one has written with greater eloquence than Cicero; and yet only a little knowledge of history is required to show that those splendid principles of which we have learnt have at no time been strictly and impartially applied. Sometimes brute force has been able to discard even the pretence of justice. More often, and perhaps more dangerously, the law has been circumvented by the skill and eloquence of the very lawyers themselves. Cicero himself is an adept at making, as the Greeks say, the worse cause appear the better. In a less brilliant way I could no doubt do the same thing myself; this facility is indeed part of our training and I have often heard Augustine deplore the fact that what he is paid to do in his profession is to provide his pupils with a weapon that may be, and is likely to be, more used for evil than for good. We learn the value of words, their possibilities for emphasis or distortion, their probable impact on various minds in various situations, and we often become intoxicated with the knowledge of the power which we have acquired. To win a case is in itself a triumph, and the more difficult the case is, the more keen is our satisfaction if we win it. There are very few teachers of rhetoric who will point out, as Augustine does, that to secure the execution of an innocent man or the acquittal of a guilty one is something of which we should be not proud, but ashamed.

Considerations of this kind have often made me feel dissatisfied with my profession, but then I think that I, and Augustine and Nebridius too, are demanding from life more clarity and sincerity than is actually to be found there. Is it not better that there should be even lip service to the idea of justice than no service at all? No lawyer, for instance, will demand the acquittal of a criminal simply because he is a criminal. He may himself know him to be one, but he will still attempt to convince the jury that he is innocent. Must one accept the conclusion that hypocrisy can be a kind of good, something better, at least, than an open contempt for the distinction between justice and injustice?

I do not feel so general a despair over the decay of our institutions, military, political and legal, as does Nebridius. I know that there are as many honest men in the world today as, except perhaps for certain periods of history and in certain situations, there ever were. All the same I cannot help agreeing with him that these institutions are, in fact, less generally accepted and approved than they were. I think that today, more than ever before, each individual man will tend to approve an honesty or a loyalty which is, as it were, purely personal or at least confined to his own particular group or sect, and that this approval is, though often sincere, often merely a justification for self-interest. A Christian, for instance, will convince himself that he has been treated unjustly if he fails to win a case in a court presided over by one who is not a Christian. I think too that a perfectly fair and upright man like Praetextatus would suspect, and often rightly, the legality of decisions reached by the emperor when advised by a synod of Christian bishops. It seems to me that justice, as we have been taught to understand it, can only exist in a society in which the vast majority will accept, or at least pretend to accept, the same or nearly the same views on morality and indeed on the nature of the world in which we live. And we do not live in such a society today. Today we are more conscious of contradiction and conflict than of agreement, and this is particularly true of the Christians who, though they claim that all men are brothers, will pursue and persecute fellow-Christians whom they regard as 'heretics' with a greater fury and vindictiveness than they show with regard to people who do not share their beliefs at all. I suppose it may be said that this passionate ardour for orthodoxy proceeds from a desire to find at last that sure and accepted groundwork of belief which, in general, we have lost and on which, in the last resort, justice itself must rest. Theoretically such an explanation is attractive and indeed there may be something in it. But how can one not be appalled at the inhumanity necessarily involved in forcibly compelling, for however good a reason, the minds of men to forsake what they believe to be the truth?

And there is another difficulty—one which I and my friends feel most acutely of all. Is there, in fact, known to us or to anyone a truth that is final and absolute? For some years Augustine and I, at any rate, believed that we had found or were on the point of finding such a truth in Manichaeism, and indeed the Manichaean picture of the whole universe engaged in a struggle between good and evil, light and darkness, does seem to correspond with much of our experience. But we have found that the correspondence is only partial and that much of what used to delight us in the doctrine is purely fanciful and in direct opposition to the findings of mathematics which, though they give us no indication of how to live our lives, are at least certain, clear and distinct. The Christians believe that truth has been revealed to them by God, and there is no logical impossibility in this. But why is it that they experience such difficulties in defining what this truth is? And who, in any case, can believe in a God who was a man with all the physical adjuncts of humanity? I respect, too, the piety and learning of people like Praetextatus and his wife; but here again I cannot be satisfied with the coherence of their beliefs. They seem to combine an intense conservatism with a willingness to accept enlightenment from any quarter from which it has ever been assumed to proceed. No doubt they believe that in all our tradition, political, legal and religious, there is something good and that this goodness is clarified and strengthened by the work of philosophers who, though they may differ among themselves, still each in his own way, throws light on one or other aspect of a many-sided reality. They are only offended by those who, like the Christians, claim a monopoly of truth and who denounce as evil spirits the Gods in whom other people believe. I think that it is impossible not to respect tradition, since we are all necessarily formed and to a large extent governed by it. Yet the mere procession of past time or even the mere longevity of a particular institution is not in itself admirable. The Epicureans can plausibly maintain that all history proceeds from the chance and meaningless collision of atoms; and some institutions, such as cannibalism or human sacrifice, are recognized to be beneath the dignity of man. And what would happen, I wonder, to the faith of Praetextatus if it were removed from the vast and apparently indestructible fabric of Rome? True that it is difficult to imagine a world in which Rome and all that she stands for is not the basis for all our activities. Yet such a condition is not unimaginable. It seems to me that the most ardent supporters of the idea of Rome tend to look backwards rather than towards the present or the future for the actuality of their ideals. Certainly all the most glowing examples of Roman virtue are looked for in the remote past. Nor is it possible to accept unreservedly the general belief in the perpetuity of Roman power. Other empires before us have risen, established themselves as though for eternity, and then been swept away. And at the present time it could be reasonably maintained that our empire (though few people will accept such an idea) is peculiarly vulnerable. According to Nebridius the Goths, if ably and ambitiously led, could, after the battle of Hadrianople, have overrun Italy and all Europe with ease. Such a situation may occur again and even, I suppose, in my lifetime, though this seems incredible.

There are some, particularly among the Christians, and perhaps, as Nebridius says, there are many who would be delighted to see this very thing happen. For they regard the world of Rome, the world of the ancient Gods and of the philosophers, as essentially evil and would see in its destruction evidence of the judgment of their own God. Most of them would assume that such an event would be the precursor of the general destruction of the whole world and the beginning of a new era, a 'heaven on earth', as they call it, in which they and those who agree precisely with them on all points of theology would live in uninterrupted bliss, while the rest of humanity would be devoted to unending torture. I see less evidence to justify such an assumption and, if I did, I would refuse to accept a view which ascribed such vindictiveness and pitilessness to the Creator.

And so, as so often in my reflections, I find myself unable to express anything but my doubt, my perplexity and my dismay. I can at least cling to the little certainty that I possess. I do know, for instance, that it is the duty of a lawyer to interpret the law honestly and so I shall have no difficulty with regard to my conduct tomorrow. I know too that whether or not I can admire the idea of Rome or applaud the structure of her greatness, whether or not I can believe in a God or discern an intelligible pattern in the universe, I do love my friends. And so I can look forward with delight to my meeting, not twenty-four hours from now, with Augustine—look forward to it, indeed, with such certain joy, that all those painful doubts and perplexities seem to me, at least for the moment, trivialities or meaningless gropings of the mind.

II

I have just spent two hours with Augustine. He wanted me to stay longer, but I could see that conversation was tiring him and I thought too that in the last half-hour of our talk he had at least partially relieved his mind of a burden and that he would be likely to enjoy a good night's sleep.

What a delight it was to both of us to be together again! The tears were running down his cheeks as we embraced and, as for me, it must have been at least a minute before I could utter a word. Indeed it was not until I had greeted Lucilla, too, and the young boy that I found myself able to frame a consecutive sentence. He was looking pale and thin, and the pallor of his face seemed to make his eyes brighter, more piercing and somehow more tragic than I remembered them; but his smile was as warm and quick as ever, and I could see that he was on the way back to health.

After we had both recovered from the first speechless glad moments of our reunion, we began to laugh at ourselves and were soon talking with all the ease and freedom of old times. After a few minutes, however, I began to notice, or to conjecture, that there was something at the back of his mind that was troubling him. I noticed this while we were discussing the illness that had struck him down almost as soon as he had arrived in Rome. He began by laughing at it and by saying that people had taken it too seriously, but I could see from his own appearance and from the expression on Lucilla's face that the illness had in fact been a dangerous one and I asked what the doctor's diagnosis of it had been. Both Augustine and Lucilla seemed embarrassed by my question. 'Oh,' said Augustine, 'it was just a fever. I suppose people get them at this time of the year.'

He was trying to keep up the light tone in which he had been speaking previously, but he did not quite succeed in doing so. He glanced away from me towards Lucilla, and there was a curious sadness in his face, almost as though he were pleading with her to show a sympathy which was not forthcoming. And she, on her side, looked at him lovingly indeed, but also showed pain in her expression, something, I thought, which was like disappointment and even a kind of bitterness.

There was a moment of silence during which all three of us were embarrassed—I, because something, and I could not imagine what, was being held back from me, they presumably, because something was preventing them from being as frank with me as they were used to being.

All this occurred in a fraction of a second, and then Augustine was smiling again at me as warmly as or even more warmly than before. I had plenty more questions to ask him, but he insisted first on asking me about myself and, at this turn in the conversation, Lucilla's face also brightened. Their interest in me and their affection were genuine enough, but they were also, I could see, relieved to be speaking on subjects where all three of us could express ourselves without constraint. 'Let us hear all about you first,' Augustine said, 'and then we'll tell you about Carthage and Nebridius and all our friends.'

Again it struck me as odd that he had made no mention of Monnica, but I knew that in the end all that I did not understand would be explained to me and so I fell in with his suggestion and began to amuse them with descriptions of my lodgings, of my landlord and of some of my colleagues in the court. Augustine questioned me closely about my work and in the course of my replies I told him about the events of the morning.

I had, of course, persisted in my opposition to the claim put forward by the senator. As I was the junior member of the court, I was asked for my opinion last and after all other members had kept the bargains which no doubt they had made with the senator's agents. It was interesting to observe the number of objections which they had succeeded in finding to the reaching of a just decision. Not one of these objections was, as they well knew, valid, but they were trying, I suppose, by a cumulation of misinterpretations to create the impression that this case, in reality so simple, was of a quite extraordinary complexity. Throughout this performance the president of the court had preserved an air of dignity, interest and understanding. He refrained from any comment and gave no indication either of agreement or disagreement with what was being said. When he asked me for my opinion I gave it in a few short sentences. The provisions of the law in this case were, I maintained (and, of course, as everyone knew), perfectly clear and none of the objections which I had heard raised seemed to me to be of sufficient force to suggest that these plain provisions should be modified in any way. After this there was some argument and, at the invitation of the president, I replied in detail to some of the points made by various members of the court. This was not difficult since, as was evident to all present, none of these points had any legal validity at all. However, my opponents were sticking to their bargain and, I think, rather enjoyed the opportunity to display their dexterity in argument and their wide reading in the works of ancient lawyers who were writing, as often as not, on cases which bore no resemblance to the one under consideration. The president himself joined eagerly in these proceedings, though without once indicating where among all these arguments his own preference lay. He showed greater learning than anyone else in his ability to quote precedents and judgments even more remote and more obscure than those which had been recalled already. Afterwards I heard someone describe his summing-up as 'a masterpiece of impartiality' and no doubt the description is just, if by 'impartiality' one means a refusal to give any sign as to where one's own opinion lies and an apparent indifference, like that assumed by the Epicureans to be enjoyed by the Gods, to what is right or wrong in any particular instance. In the whole discussion it seemed that nearly everyone was enjoying the atmosphere of unreality. For unless I withdrew my objections (which I was not going to do), the case would be automatically dismissed. Meanwhile those who had been influenced by bribery or intimidation were acting as they had been instructed to do and could not reasonably be blamed if their efforts to distort justice turned out unsuccessfully. Indeed many of them, including the president, were, I think, happy at the way things were going, since in general they would prefer justice to be done if it could be done without injury to themselves. So, finally, I doubt whether I made more than a few enemies among my colleagues. Indeed one of them, when the case was over, came up to me and, when he was sure that he was out of hearing of the rest, almost congratulated me on my behaviour. 'I myself,' he said, 'should certainly have taken up the same line as you, if I had been in your position. But', he went on with a smile, 'you must remember that all of us have not your advantages. You might, by the way, mention my name to Praetextatus when you see him next. I once served with him for a short time when he was governor of Achaea. Perhaps he may remember me.'

This speech had shocked and pained me. I saw that most of my colleagues believed that I would not have ventured to take the stand I did if I had not been assured of the support of a protector much more powerful than was the senator who had so overawed them. In fact I had not even thought of Praetextatus in this connection, but I could see that it was perfectly true that, if I had approached him on the question, he would certainly have encouraged me to act as I had done. He would also, of course, have thought less well of me for being afraid to act honestly unless I was first guaranteed immunity, and this in itself would have deterred me from even mentioning the case to him, supposing that I had thought of doing so. But I doubted whether any of my colleagues would have believed this and I saw too that in fact I was (though I had not realized it) in a more secure position than any of them had been in. And so, even though I was not consciously aware of it, this fact in itself rather than any genuine honesty in myself might have determined my conduct. I had to acknowledge too that I had felt a certain pride in what I imagined to have been my own rectitude. What miserable creatures we are, so apt to condemn others, so unwilling to admit our own weaknesses!

I was attempting to express these thoughts to Augustine, but, as I might have known would happen, he refused to listen to me, although, if it had been his own conduct that was under consideration, he would have doubted his own motives just as I was doubting mine; indeed he would have exercised powers of self-analysis much greater than any which I possess, and, very likely, would have condemned himself more completely than I was prepared to do in my own case. As it was, he had nothing for me but praise and affection. He clasped my hand and again the tears ran down his face as he spoke. 'Alypius,' he said, 'what a delight and what an example you are to all of us! You always know what is right to do and you never hesitate in doing it. Nearly everyone would have found some excuse for himself for acting unjustly and so either doing himself good or avoiding some possible injury. But to you such an idea simply would not occur. You know perfectly well that, whether you had had powerful friends or not, you would have acted just as you did. I hope that I would have done the same thing, but, if I had, I should have had to struggle to be brave and to struggle in order not to put my own ambitions before justice. But with you I know there was no struggle. Oh, how I wish that I could be simple and true like you are!'

Augustine's voice is extraordinarily expressive and in this last sentence of his there was so much evident sadness that I was at a loss how to answer him. Normally I should have laughed at him and told him how very partial his estimate of me was. For indeed he thinks much more highly of me than I deserve. He does not know yet, for instance, how for a short time I had been again swept away by that mad and brutal love of bloodshed in the arena and of how I had indeed struggled against it and had eventually been liberated not by my own efforts but in some way which I still do not understand. Now, however, as I heard that note of anguish in his voice, it seemed to me that this was no time for arguments about myself and the 'purity' which he so often attributes to me. I looked at him with surprise and, probably, with consternation, waiting for him to proceed, and he, as he always does, noticed immediately the alteration in my looks. He smiled and, for no easily apparent reason, said, 'I am sorry.'

Lucilla also, I am sure, had observed the despair that had been in his voice and no doubt she knew the reason for it. She smiled kindly at me and smiled also, though more timidly, at Augustine. Then she left the room, taking the boy Adeodatus with her.

As soon as she had gone Augustine again clasped my hand in a quick gesture of affection. And now he began to speak more calmly, still sadly, but without the pain that is caused by constraint. 'My dear friend,' he said, 'forgive me for my selfishness. Somehow I could not help contrasting myself with you, and envying you. You are too good to hurt anyone, and all that you do gives pleasure to those whom you love. But I go on hurting people and it is the people whom I love whom I hurt most.'

I saw that he was speaking of Monnica and asked him about her. He looked quickly at me and smiled, grateful, evidently, that I had introduced her name, 'Yes,' he said, 'of course it was of her that I was thinking, and also of Lucilla.'

Still, however, he seemed to hesitate before explaining the particular circumstances that were distressing him. 'Why is it,' he said, 'that the only people whom I injure deeply are women? It is not that they love me any more than you do, or

Nebridius does. But they want all of me and I cannot distribute my whole self.'

'Maybe,' I said, 'you want all of each of them too. But with you and me and Nebridius we are happy or sad together. We are not jealous of each other.'

'You are right,' he said. 'And if one of us makes a new friend he wants the others to love that friend too. But with women it is different. Lucilla, for instance, is glad that my mother is not here.'

I saw the look of pain that came over his face when he spoke the words 'my mother'. But I am fond of Lucilla and, though what he said was undoubtedly true, it seemed to me that he might be condemning her unjustly. 'I have often thought,' I said, 'that Monnica also would be glad if Lucilla were not with you.'

He appeared surprised at my words and this struck me as curious, since I imagine that Lucilla must very often have said just the same thing to him. For a moment he seemed pained and I fancied that he was about to contradict me. But then he shook his head quickly and almost impatiently in a gesture with which I am very familiar. He uses it quite involuntarily when he is dismissing from his mind some thought or idea which may have lodged there and pleased him, but which he suddenly finds to be untrue or unsatisfactory.

'Yes,' he said, 'it is so. And she can give what appears to be good reasons for feeling as she does. She says that Lucilla is a handicap to me in my career, and—what moves me more than that—she says that my excessive devotion to the pleasures of love is in itself something bad, something that must tend to draw me further and further away from the God in whom she believes and from the wisdom which I have been determined to seek ever since my nineteenth year, when I read the *Hortensius* of Cicero, the wisdom which you too, Alypius, but with how much more purity, are seeking. And I feel that she is speaking the truth. But I tell her that there have been many good and wise men who have been married and

132

who, presumably, have enjoyed the same pleasures as I do. She replies that indeed marriage may be a good thing, but that in marriage the pleasures are totally different from any that I know. Marriage, she says, is for the sake and good of others, for the deliberate bearing of children and, finally, not for the love or the gratification of a body, but for the love of God. And again I feel that there is truth in her words. For my own feelings are not like those which she describes. I cling to this pleasure just for itself and I cannot go a day without it. Or would it be truer to say that this pleasure clings to me, distracting me from what I dimly see to be good, dazzling my eyes with its sweetness, hurrying me away in its velocity? As you know, I never wanted to have a child at all. It was the pleasure and only the pleasure that I wanted.'

'And yet,' I said, 'when the boy was born, you and Lucilla immediately fell in love with him. You have loved Adeodatus and cared for him at least as well as any married people care for their children. You know yourself how proud you are of his intelligence and how many hours you have spent on developing it. His birth may have been an accident, but his upbringing has been a work of love.'

He was listening to me intently and as though he wanted to agree with me. But again he shook his head. 'No,' he said, 'you do not understand, Alypius, you are too pure and good yourself to see the utter selfishness of others. Of course I am glad of Adeodatus and of course I love him. Who could help it? But if someone were to say, "he was conceived in sin", I should have to agree. He was. Neither of us wanted him. What we wanted was simply constant and continual enjoyment of the ecstatic pleasures of the senses, pleasures that are sweet indeed, utterly overpowering, often brutal, often when one looks back at them, merely disgusting. Later, certainly, I loved him, but what did I love in him? Perhaps merely an extension of myself, a kind of immortality, and an intelligence keener than my own, for the existence of which I was somehow mysteriously responsible.'

Here he paused and I could see that what he was saying was merely the prelude to something else which he wanted to say. Indeed so far he was saying nothing that he had not said often to me before. I personally believe that in all this he is judging himself too strictly, for what I see in his love for Lucilla and the boy is good, so that I have often wished that I myself could be in such a position. But when I argue to this effect, he will tell me that, because of my way of life, I cannot understand his predicament and he will congratulate me on what he calls my 'purity'. Now, however, it was evident that there was some other subject which he was trying to introduce. He did not reach it immediately.

'In my heart,' he said, 'I recognize that what my mother says is true. But I do not wish to accept that truth. And the way I avoid accepting it is by supposing that in what she says she is motivated by the wrong reasons. I see as well as you do that she is jealous of my affection for Lucilla and that in a sense this jealousy is merely the jealousy of a woman who longs to hold and to absorb entirely the attention and the love of a man. So far as jealousy and possessiveness are concerned there is no difference between Lucilla's feelings for me as a lover and my mother's feelings for me as a son. And I must own that my own feelings are equally jealous and equally possessive with regard to the women (but not, as I said, the men) whom I love. I could not bear it if Lucilla were to become the mistress of another man; and I am happy (though if I were more generous, I should not be) that my mother loves me more than her other children. I see, or I think that I see, that this devouring and relentless and possessive love, whether it is the love of a son, or of a lover, is less high and noble than is that unselfish love which does not seek power, does not seek anything except the good of its object. And at this point I am swept away by my own dishonesty which acts as a shield and cover for my lust. Because I convince myself that what my mother says about my love for Lucilla is said for the wrong reason, I go on to take the wholly unjustifiable step of concluding that what she says is not true. What a childish and disgusting piece of self-deception! As though truth is any the less true, for whatever motives it may be stated! But I, the I who imagines himself to be pursuing wisdom will go to any length to reject a truth which conflicts with the habitual demands of my senses. And what is the result? I wanted happiness, the kind of happiness which we are used to, for Lucilla and for myself. But I have made her more unhappy than before, because she can see how unwilling my will really is. And as for my mother, I have behaved towards her like a coward and a traitor. I have hurt her, perhaps irreparably.'

While he was speaking he showed the intense agitation of his mind not so much by any gesture or any incoherence as by the modulations of his voice and by the emphasis he gave to certain words. He had scarcely looked at me once, but now he raised his head. I could see the distress in his eyes, but I could also see that he had reached the point at which he had been aiming and that it would be a relief to him now to tell me what had happened.

He did so comparatively calmly and in a few words. It seems that when he had decided to come to Rome, Monnica had been anxious to accompany him and had once again begged him to leave Lucilla behind. She herself, she had said, would be happy to look after the child, and, without Lucilla, Augustine would be able to make an honourable marriage into a good family. She had employed all the arguments which he had already mentioned, and many more besides. It was not surprising that Lucilla should have resented the suggestion nor that Augustine should have been unwilling to comply with it. But when Monnica had seen what his attitude was, she had none the less insisted on accompanying him, in spite of the fact that the hostility between herself and Lucilla had now become more open than veiled. Augustine owned that what in particular made him averse from Monnica's plan was the prospect of living in a household where a constant state of tension would prevail. It would be hard enough in any case to cut out a new career for himself in Rome and the task, he thought, would be not only difficult, but impossible, if he were never to enjoy a moment's peace in his private life. Also he feared the effect of the long sea voyage on his mother's health and, knowing that she had never left Africa in her life and indeed never even left Thagaste except to stay with him in Carthage, he could not imagine her as being happy in a wholly different environment. Now, of course, he dismissed these arguments as mere hypocrisy, but I believe that here again he is judging himself too harshly. These feelings were genuine, even though they were not the ones that mainly determined his conduct. However, nothing that he could say would deter Monnica from doing what she had decided to do. She would leave Africa, leave her daughter and her other son and all her friends gladly; she would even pretend to tolerate Lucilla, so long as she could be with Augustine.

As for him, he had never spoken an angry word to her in his life and now he found it quite impossible to make it wholly clear to her what his resolution was. For he had in fact decided to leave her behind. In this way he would at least, he thought, make Lucilla happy and perhaps himself too—perhaps even his mother, if in the course of time she could become reconciled to his absence. 'But I knew,' he now said, 'of course I knew, that this could not be. And now I have made everyone unhappy.'

His last effort had been to persuade Monnica to stay behind in Africa until he had been able to find suitable lodgings in Rome, when he would send for her if she still wished to be with him. This plan had distressed Lucilla and his mother equally. 'And how do I know,' he said to me, 'whether I was sincere even in this?'

Monnica had insisted on travelling with him all the way to the coast, often imploring him with tears to come back with her, often asserting that, if he would not do so, she would buy herself a passage on the same boat as that on which he and

Lucilla were travelling. And now occurred the incident of which he was most ashamed. I could see that though it hurt him to speak of it, he was still relieved when he had done so.

Near the place where they were staying on the court was a chapel dedicated to the memory of the Christian bishop Cyprian. Augustine had persuaded his mother to spend the evening at this chapel, telling her that he had to go down to the post to say goodbye to a friend who was setting out on a voyage to Alexandria. Since he had never told her a lie before she believed him and went away with other Christians to visit the chapel and no doubt to pray for her son. Meanwhile he, Lucilla and the boy had hurriedly gone aboard the ship and were out on the open sea and on their way to Rome before Monnica could have suspected the deception which had been practised on her.

Since then, as I could well believe, he had had no peace Thoughts of his mother's distress and of his own cowardly betrayal of her had taken away any rest he might have enjoyed in the present or any ambition for the future. And Lucilla, who had been prepared to be happy and at last in some sense secure, had been deprived by his own unhappiness of all that she had looked forward to. 'When I was ill and delirious,' he said, 'I was, I suppose, most happy, and this was because I was not myself at all. But now the thought of that illness, which seemed merciful at the time, fills me with horror. Suppose that I had died then. The last action of my life would have been that very action which of all others must be most hateful to me—the wounding of a mother, the betrayal of so much love. And in whatever life there may be after this one, how appalling would be my state! I would have deserved every torture that poets and philosophers imagine. And, if there is an eternity of existence, I should have been separated for ever from what is good, set in some different world from that which my mother would inhabit, though even in that world of bliss where she would be I should still be hurting her, for she would still and for ever feel the pain I had inflicted on her and would still be weeping for me.'

Here he stopped and I said what I could to comfort him. To me it seemed that Monnica's own conduct had not been altogether blameless and that, indefensible as his deception of her might be, it was something to which she herself, in a sense, had driven him. But I knew that no useful purpose would be served by saying such things as this. He had undoubtedly made these excuses to himself already and had, rightly or wrongly, utterly dismissed them. All I could do now, it seemed, was to make him feel the assurance of my sympathy and friendship, and I could see that already, though his distress was as great as ever, he had benefited from being able to speak openly to me. I regarded it as likely, indeed as almost certain, that he would now beg Monnica to join him in Rome at the earliest opportunity. This thought made me feel sorry for Lucilla and, though I try to assure myself that, after this experience, Monnica will be more tolerant of her than before, I cannot honestly believe that this will be so.

I did not see Lucilla again before I left and now, as I write, I find myself thinking of her as much as of Augustine himself. She will be glad, I think, to find him more relaxed than he was and he will be kinder and gentler to her than ever. But it will not be the perfect kindness and the perfect gentleness which she wants. Why is it that this love between man and woman is so cruel in its consequences?

III

Weeks have gone by since I last wrote down any account of my thoughts and doings. I have felt no need to do so and this, I suppose, is because every day I have visited Augustine or he has visited me, and I can express myself to him more clearly than I can to myself. It has been just like the old days in Carthage; indeed our pleasure in seeing each other has been, because of our long separation and our rediscovery of the affection which holds us together, even greater than before.

I myself have had an additional source of pleasure in watching my friend recover his health so quickly and completely. And I have enjoyed showing him the principal sights of Rome and watching his reactions to the actual presence of all the memorials of that long history of hers which we studied at school but which seemed to us in Africa, though real enough, still somehow remote from us. I am prepared to believe that there are more beautiful buildings in Athens and equally grand ones in Constantinople and Alexandria. Even in Carthage we have temples, libraries and theatres which can compare with the best in Rome. But can there be anywhere except Rome where one is so conscious of the depth and weight and power of history? Here one can walk along the very street up which from the time of the early republic to the present day have gone the triumphal processions of victorious generals. One can stand in the very spot from which Caesar or Cicero addressed the Roman people. One can visit portions of the same walls which shut out Hannibal from the rewards of his victories. And then, more numerous than the buildings of the republic, many of which have been destroyed by fire, there are the vast monuments of the empire. There are the parks and gardens in some of which the bodies of Christians were burned like torches by the mad Emperor Nero who, to divert suspicion from himself, had accused this obscure sect of having caused the great fire of Rome. There are the huge baths of Caracalla, the vast amphitheatre, temples of Isis, chapels dedicated to the blood baptism of Mithra and the new Christian churches with their frescoes of the appalling tortures of the martyrs in this world and of their persecutors in the next. There seems to be an infinite variety of religion, of race and of occupation. Fantastic luxury and the utmost squalor are juxtaposed. Priests who worship a King of Peace, and soldiers, Roman, Spanish, Gothic, German, who live by warfare, jostle each other in the streets. And all this, in its continuity of tradition, in its weird variety and contradiction, is Rome, the centre and mistress of the world.

Augustine is as moved as I am by the splendour of the present and by the weight and elaboration of the history which it represents. But he, even more than I am, is conscious of a lack not, certainly, of vitality, but of something like reality. There are still consuls; the fire still burns in the temple of Vesta. But in fact the government of the empire is carried on elsewhere, in Milan or Constantinople. Politics and patriotism, in the sense understood by Cicero, by Cato or by Caesar, have ceased to exist, at least here. Their places have been taken by entertainment and by religious controversy. And even these, which would appear so disparate, the one a field for apathy, the other for ambition, are today strangely intermingled in a manner that would be incomprehensible not only to a philosopher but to any Roman of the old days. Particular charioteers, gladiators, actors or actresses will have each his or her own vociferous following which will depend on which particular religious belief he or she holds or is presumed to hold, so that a performer will be applauded not only for his skill but equally or more for his adherence to the view that, in Christian terminology, the Son is either equal or not equal with the Father.

We have talked often on the subject of religion and I find that Augustine is as distressed as I am by the fact that we can find no certainty anywhere. He had lost all faith in the basic teachings of Mani and he had already weakened the faith of the once ardent Manichaean at whose house he is still staying. But he owns that he can find no other faith equally attractive or more certain and he still spends much time in the company of various members, including some of the 'elders', of the Manichaean community in Rome. There is a certain modesty about them, he says, which he does not find either among the Christians or among the professional philosophers. For the Christians believe fiercely and ardently in what are plain impossibilities and most of the philosophers too are so determined to vindicate their own particular scheme of things that they are blind to other and equally valid interpretations of reality. Perhaps he is now most attracted by the writings of the Academic school of philosophy who admit that it is impossible to be perfectly certain about anything and, having made this admission, go on to inquire what beliefs are on the whole less uncertain than others or more conducive to human welfare. But he will readily admit that, though he can see nothing better than this line of inquiry, this is not what he would like to see. I think that he will demand certainty, as he has always done, and that he will not be happy until he finds it. Here I certainly sympathize with him, though I know that my feelings are not so intense as his are. I think that I could be happy, so long as I was with my friends, simply in inquiring into truth and I could be content to be only partially satisfied in my inquiry. But for Augustine a partial satisfaction is no satisfaction at all. He often speaks to me longingly of his mother's complete certainty in her convictions and he would wish to be like her, if he could. But of course his keen mind is repelled by the philosophical absurdities of many Christian beliefs and his cultivated literary taste is equally repelled by the roughness or the childish simplicity of style in which these beliefs are expressed. Not that he will ever accuse Monnica of either fanaticism or of insensibility. He admires her and his admiration and love have become all the stronger because of the guilt he feels for what he calls his betrayal of her at the time when he left her behind in Africa.

Here things have happened very much as I expected. He has written to ask her to join him in Rome and she has promised to do so in the spring. The prospect of seeing her again and the fact that she has forgiven him for an action of which he is himself so deeply ashamed have made her dearer to him than ever. For all the difficulties and for all the tension which prevailed in his household in Africa he now blames himself and only himself. Thus he is able to convince himself that this state of tension has been permanently relieved and that the same difficulties will not recur. He even thinks that Lucilla takes the same view of the situation as he does; but this I find hard to believe. He may well hope that he is right and she herself, being satisfied, or at least largely satisfied, with Augustine's devotion to her, will certainly not do anything which she knows would displease him. She may even, in order to keep him happy, pretend to be more fond of his mother than she is. Indeed she might well be fond of Monnica if she did not fear her so much. And it seems to me that she has reason to fear her. She has said as much to me, on the few occasions when we have been alone together and, though I try to reassure her, I do not think that my words carry much conviction.

It seems to me a strange and a sad thing that between friends who are normally sincere and outspoken with each other some kind of barrier will arise, some feeling of secrecy or mistrust, whenever one of them becomes involved in the affections of women, however natural these affections may be. Here, and perhaps here only, men, and women too, seem to be wholly satisfied with the validity of their own judgments and, if they do seek the opinion of another, they will resent or dismiss it unless it coincides precisely with their own. I, for instance, though I am younger and less intelligent than Augustine, can speak perfectly freely to him if I consider that he is making a mistake in his interpretation of a passage of poetry, in his judgment of a man's character or in the organization of his work. Usually I am wrong, but sometimes I am right, and then, so far from resenting my interposition, he will be glad and grateful for it. But I know that if I were to go out of my way to express to him my true feelings about Monnica and Lucilla, if I were to say, for instance, 'Monnica will never be satisfied until you have got rid of Lucilla. Do you want that?', such an intervention would be wholly useless and might, indeed, do more harm than good. He would not resent my words, because he would know that they were spoken sincerely and he resents nothing that I say. He would simply not admit them into his mind, and this in spite of the fact that they express what he himself must often have thought. No doubt he would tell me that I do not understand and in particular that I cannot possibly understand the strong sexual bond that unites him to Lucilla. This may be true, but it is also true that, though he understands Virgil better than I do, there are still some occasions when on a particular passage my understanding is more acute than his. And on such subjects, however much he might be entitled to do so, he would never say, 'You don't understand.' Instead, whether in the end he accepted my view or not, he would at any rate examine it carefully and objectively.

I find it very difficult satisfactorily to explain this attitude of his. Of course it is easy to say that on a matter so dear to him he half fears that what I say is true, that he is reluctant to admit that possibility and that therefore he refuses, from cowardice or from prejudice, even to allow what I have to say to enter into his mind. There may even be some truth in this explanation, but it is far from being the whole truth. For Augustine is not cowardly and he is not prejudiced. He is the most honest man I have ever known. May it be, I wonder, that in some matters affection and even passion must precede, in the sense of being logically prior to, reason? In poetry, for instance, unless I feel intimately in my own heart the force and beauty of a particular line or passage, no amount of critical exposition can have any meaning for me. Only after I have loved the poetry for itself can I attempt to understand the meaning of my love, to justify it and to compare it with other elements in my experience. Gradually, no doubt, my taste becomes more refined by criticism and comparison. I may in the end reject as sentimental or bombastic passages which I once admired. But it will not be by purely rational means that I shall have reached the point where I reject what I once loved, even though reason will have played a part in the process. Reason can help to explain why one love is inferior to another, but it can only do this when one had already loved what is superior.

And so on certain matters it may be that truth itself must depend on depth and strength of feeling. To be wholly satisfactory it must, of course, not offend against reason; but without feeling it cannot be grasped at all. And Augustine may be right when, with regard to his personal emotions, he tells me that I do not understand. When we are discussing a passage in Virgil or a theory in philosophy or music or the character of others we are, as it were, standing on the same ground, united by the affection we feel for each other and by the shared interest in or enthusiasm for the subject under discussion. But unless I were physically in love with Lucilla or physically the son of Monnica, I could never share his feelings with regard to them. Thus, however adequate my reasoning, it would lack one essential element, the element of passion. Even supposing I am right in believing that his love for Lucilla and his love for Monnica are incompatible, nothing that I could say will convince him of this, and even if I did convince him, I should make him unhappier than before. Were I to tell him that it would be better if Monnica were to remain in Africa, he would say, quite rightly, that I was thinking more of his happiness than of hers; and he could go on to say, also rightly, that I cannot fully understand how much even his own happiness is bound up with hers.

And suppose I were to advise him to do as his mother would wish and to give up Lucilla. I put this as a hypothetical case, since I know that I could not give this advice. For, though I may not be able perfectly to understand either her feelings or his, I can imagine the pain that both he and she would suffer if they were separated. No doubt Augustine can imagine it even more clearly and agonizingly than I can; and yet I think that if I were to repeat to him the arguments already used by his mother against Lucilla, he would be more likely to listen to me than he would be if I were to belittle those arguments and to urge him, if he has to choose, to choose Lucilla's interests rather than Monnica's. Of course he is attempting to convince himself that there is no such necessity of choice and I hope that he is right, though certainly the evidence of the past is against him.

But if, as I think probable, he does find in the end that these two powerful affections are indeed incompatible, what is it that will decide him to inflict pain on one rather than on the other of the two women whom he loves? Who can tell what precise parts will be played here by vanity, by custom, by ambition, by passion, by the longing for what is superior and by the zeal for integrity? And however carefully one may analyse the strength of various aspects of his motivation, how can one know if one's analysis is at all true? How often do we present to ourselves and accept as true an explanation for our conduct which disguises rather than reveals our real motive! Not that Augustine would ever consciously or half-consciously deceive himself. For any pain he causes or suffers, for any disability or impediment in his life, he is more apt to blame himself than to blame either people or circumstance. But in this dilemma which I am imagining neither honesty nor reason would seem to provide any sure guidance. For he will, if I am right (and I hope that I am not), have to choose between two things both of which are good, and whatever his choice may be, it will cause pain to himself, and to one whom he loves.

I think that what may finally determine him is something that may be called a sense of shame, though quite why he feels this I do not know. But his love for Monnica, apart from the relief and pleasure which he finds in it, seems to him voluntary and, as he would say, 'pure'; whereas, intense as his passion for Lucilla is, there is something in it which disturbs him. He did not choose it; rather it chose him and sweeps him away. And since it is not under his control, he somehow resents it. He feels that the sexual appetite is, though more powerful than hunger or thirst, still something of the same nature as these, an impulse which we share with the beasts and something of an altogether different order from the disinterested affection we feel for our friends or from the love of wisdom. This, of course, is the view of the Manichaeans and of the Christians, though the Christians will regard the act of sex as being legitimate and even to some extent sanctified if it results in the propagation of children, while the Manichaeans take the precisely opposite view and say that if the appetite is irresistible it is best indulged in some way which will not result in child-bearing; some indeed commend homosexuality as the purest expression of this instinct. However, the two sects, and many others too, do have this in common—that they regard sexual passion as, at best, regrettable and, at the worst, positively evil.

I used to hold this view too, but now I am not so certain of it. Since I became able to recall to myself exactly that visit of mine, of which I felt so ashamed, to the brothel in Madaura, what stands out most clearly in my mind is the moment of perfect peace, security and even love which I experienced with that girl just before the whole scene was transformed into one of horror and disgust. For the peace was as real as the horror and I had acquired this peace through the body and by means of this instinct which is so generally deplored. I, of course, had no real love for the girl and she even less for me, and yet my body led me into love, at least for a second or two. Might not this experience be very much more profound and lasting, something indeed perfectly satisfactory, if it is shared by two people who are genuinely and purely devoted to each other, as Augustine and Lucilla are, or seem to be?

Here, of course, as on so many other subjects, my lack of knowledge prevents me from any confidence, and I must own that Augustine, who ought to know, does not appear to think of these matters in the same way as that in which I have begun to think. For whatever reason it may be, he lacks a perfect confidence in his passion and it is largely because of this that his mother is likely to have a more potent influence on him than Lucilla herself.

Personally, though I like and admire Monnica, I am glad that some months must go by before she arrives. I can see that Lucilla dreads her coming, though she attempts to hide her feelings. I wonder too whether Augustine is as sure as he pretends to be that the future relationship between the two women will be more harmonious than it was before?

IV

Again I have let months pass without writing anything in this notebook and again the reason for this is that in our almost daily conversations I have been able to share all my thoughts and impressions with Augustine. This has been a relief and a pleasure to me; and yet, greatly as we both enjoy the freedom and ease of our friendship, it would be wrong, I think, to say that either of us is content. More than five years have gone by since he and I and Nebridius pledged ourselves to the pursuit of wisdom and truth. And are we any nearer to the object of our search? Are we not indeed further away than ever? In those days we were young and enthusiastic; we felt that we could rely on the keenness of our intelligences and on the sincerity of our purpose; and so, while admitting the difficulties of our task, we still had a certain confidence that it would be, at least to some extent, rewarded. Now we are still young in years and still sincere in our endeavour; but it seems that we are increasingly visited by premonitions of despair. There are still, no doubt, systems of religion and of philosophy which we have not examined and it may be possible, I suppose, to imagine that in one or other of these we shall find the answers to our questions and the certainty which we demand. Yet somehow this solution appears less and less likely. All systems of philosophy interest me and some arouse my admiration; yet often what I admire is little more than an intellectual, or even a verbal, dexterity—something not so very different from what I observe every day in the law courts. In all of them, except perhaps for the philosophy of Plato, there is a certain aridity or petrifaction. There is nothing to love or to worship. Even in Plato what charms me is not so much the philosophy itself, but the presentation of it. I am more moved by the character of Socrates himself—his kindness, his integrity, his wit and charm—than by the idea of the Good, which I cannot understand.

Among religious people too I find much to admire and even to envy. Monnica, for instance, is utterly devoted to the Christian God and is perfectly certain that her devotion and belief are justified. But so are the addicts of any superstition and if a belief is harmless or even beneficial, it does not follow that it is true. Though again I ought not to dismiss a belief simply because it is held by somewhat simple-minded people. Monnica, certainly, is not remarkably intelligent and lacks the education of Augustine or even myself; yet I must admit that many intelligent people have held the same beliefs as she. Jerome, for instance, or Ambrose, the Bishop of Milan, have the reputation of being extremely distinguished scholars. What I canot understand is how they can possibly believe in what seems to me, however I examine it, plainly impossible.

And my bewilderment is increased when I consider other men, Praetextatus for instance, who are just as intelligent as Jerome or Ambrose and who believe equally devoutly in the old Gods. Philosophically they, and also the Manichaeans, are more attractive than the Christians, because they believe that God can be revealed in very many different ways and will admit that Jesus also is a vehicle of truth and understanding, while the Christians denounce every faith except their own as being not only untrue, but positively evil. To them Mithra, Isis, Ceres and the rest are demons. But how what they imagine to be a perfectly good and omnipotent God can have created evil beings is something which they do not explain. Certainly Praetextatus and those like him are more tolerant and more rational. Also they live lives that are as pure and upright as those of any Christians. Yet there are articles in their belief which seem to me more crude and savage than any to be found in Christianity. How can there be any divinity in the obscene pantomimes which accompany the processions in honour of Flora? And though, from the little I know of the subject, I can imagine there to be dignity and enlightenment in the mysteries of Isis or of Ceres, the baths in the blood of a ram or a bull, which are so important a part of the worship of Mithra, seem to me merely disgusting.

Who am I, I often ask myself, to reject beliefs which are sincerely held by men who are clearly better and wiser than myself? Since I desire certainty so much, ought I not to be content to follow others who have greater experience and greater knowledge than my own? A man cannot know everything and I, a young and ignorant man, cannot know very much, and I rightly accept much on the testimony of others. I have never, for instance, seen Britain with my own eyes; yet I believe it to exist and to be more or less as it is described by travellers who have been there. Ought I not in the same way to accept, however blindly, religious beliefs which have been found true by others?

Many people do, in fact, adopt just this procedure—perhaps I should be glad to do so too, if I could. There is something noble and satisfying in such expressions as 'the Gods of our fathers', as though a long tradition in itself established the validity of a belief. But in these matters tradition, however venerable, cannot constitute proof or disarm scepticism. Who, after all, are 'the Gods of our fathers'? Of all the good and wise men I know or have heard of who have been sincerely devoted to a religion, one half would declare the rest to be wholly and utterly mistaken.

Very often recently Augustine and I have discussed the possibility that we ourselves may be carried away by a kind of enthusiasm for an object which does not exist. The wisdom and happiness on which we have set ourselves may be in the nature of things unattainable. Perfection may not exist and the utmost that we can hope for may be to be able to distinguish between what is more and what is less untrue or unworthy. As it is we find the world about us to be on the whole alien and displeasing. May this not be simply because we have failed to adapt ourselves to it? We imagine, for instance, that in the past, before the empire covered half the world and before its organization became so remote and so intricate as to be almost incomprehensible, life was simpler and more noble, patriotism and religion were realities. But is there any evidence for this? Is it not true that the world has always been much the same in essentials as it is now; that motives have always been united; that no one has ever been perfectly happy? And in this state of imperfection have there not always been, and are there not now, opportunities for a genuine, if limited, satisfaction?

In friendship alone, it has often seemed to me, there is such peace and delight to be found that one ought to be content with its simple and continual enjoyment. And I see no good reason to believe (though here Augustine, who knows more, disagrees) that the same and even a more intense enjoyment may be found in the love which binds a man and a woman together. Certainly I know that the affection which Augustine and I feel for each other is something true and good and satisfying. It is not confined by rules, like politics or the law. It is warm where philosophy is cold. It is clear and genuine were religion is muddy, savage or self-contradictory. And yet still we look beyond it and however satisfied we are with our feelings for each other we feel, I think, a certain sense of isolation, as though it were a case of two men trying to keep warm in a world of ice, or joyfully clasping hands in the middle of an infinite desert. Somehow it is necessary for the world also to be warm, the world also to be comprehensible. For if it were not, it would seem that even our genuine enjoyment is merely a gesture of defiance or of despair.

We are indeed connected with this alien world. This is the human condition. The structure of our bodies, hunger and thirst, language, civilization, profession, all inevitably bind us together with others. And some people find something approaching a real freedom in this bondage. Praetextatus, for instance, is one who can be called happy. He has friends, a wife whom he loves, wealth, power, honour. He is a scholar, a philosopher, a general and an administrator. He has a religion in which he believes. In a few weeks' time he will become praetorian prefect, a position in the state only second to that of the emperor. He deserves his honours and he will carry them with modesty. He enjoys his work and he will do it well. Everyone admires him except the more extreme Christians, who, because of his sincere devotion to the old religion, regard him as some kind of demon.

But would I, assuming the unlikely case that I were to possess all his merits and all his abilities, care to be in his position? I find that I would not, even though I know him to be so much better a man than I am. But how can it be that I should seem to prefer what is unsatisfactory in myself to what

I can see to be satisfactory in him? It would be absurd to say that every man has an equal right to his own opinion on every subject and a duty to cling to this opinion. A man who has never read Homer cannot have any opinion on that subject at all. Nor am I anxious to be in any way exceptional, or to prove to my own satisfaction and that of others a superiority of intellect or character which I know that I do not possess. Yet still I cannot assent to what I cannot believe. I can admire the goodness and integrity of Praetextatus' life and can even try to imitate it; but I cannot share in many of those serious beliefs which, in the end, support and strengthen him in his goodness and integrity. His religion seems to me mere superstition, his patriotism a form of antiquarianism. For the empire, it seems to me, is falling apart and the Gods are dying. What remains to be admired and emulated are the ordinary virtues which have been honoured everywhere and always by all men—justice, integrity, honesty, efficiency, kindness. Why is it that, though I too honour these virtues, I still demand something more? What I demand, as does Augustine, is that these virtues should be shown to be part of the fabric of the universe or, at least, of the society in which we live. And what I call the superstition and the antiquarianism of Praetextatus do at least enable him to believe that they are.

We, on the other hand, who reject his fundamental beliefs, must remain restless and unsatisfied until we can find beliefs of our own which we can hold with an equal conviction. And for years now we have strained our intellects and our emotions vainly and inconclusively. Our satisfactions are in our friendship and in our work. In our friendship we can believe absolutely, as in a certain good. And we derive pleasure from doing our work well; though here the pleasure is not unmixed, for what is the final aim of our work?

I attempt, certainly, to interpret the law correctly and this is a valuable task, since the structure of society must depend on a fair and equal administration of justice. And although in our legal practice there is plenty of room for all kinds of fraud and chicanery, although some laws are antiquated and their strict administration may often encourage the very abuses which they were designed to correct, on the whole the main principles of legal justice are at least acknowledged and are, much more often than not, followed. Yet even in our justice there is something lacking. Much of my own work is taken up solely with the extraction of as much money as possible from as many sources as are available. This money is used to finance the operations of the empire, many of which are, of course, valuable and useful. But the average tax-payer is completely ignorant of what these operations are, and is, as a rule, completely indifferent to them. Laws are no longer designed, as they used to say, to make men better. They often seem to me to exist simply for the protection or exploitation of property, or for the maintenance of a state of apathy.

Augustine works harder than I do and is better known in his profession. Moreover his work may be held to be at least as important as mine, since he is training in speech, in appreciation, in science, literature and philosophy those who will be the lawyers, administrators and scholars of the future. He has already a considerable reputation in Rome and he began by enjoying his work here much more than he had enjoyed it in Carthage. The students, he tells me, are better behaved, more ambitious and at least equally intelligent. Recently, indeed, he has become somewhat disillusioned. Though the young men of Rome are good students and behave in a more mannerly way than the often rowdy and irresponsible youth of Carthage, they are very reluctant to pay the fees for their tuition and have devised numbers of tricks by which to avoid payment. A whole class, for instance, may towards the end of a course which they have been attending suddenly leave their professor and go off to join the class of another, whom again they will leave when the time comes for them to pay their fees. All that the professor can do is to try to recover by legal means the money that is due to him, and this is a long and costly operation. And of course professors who are just starting in business or who are not very sought-after in any case are likely to accept what pupils come their way, even if they do not feel confident that they will be paid. Augustine has not suffered from this kind of dishonesty anything like so much as have others. He has very soon acquired the reputation of being one of the best teachers in Rome, so that people are anxious to study under him and he can now afford to demand payment in advance. But he is disgusted by the dishonesty which makes it necessary for him to do this. Worse still, he is becoming more and more disgusted with the job itself and for much the same reasons as I am sometimes dissatisfied with my own job. He knows that he is an exceptionally brilliant teacher and, however hard he works, he can fully enjoy it when he finds a pupil who is seriously interested in poetry or philosophy for its own sake. Instead of this, however, he finds that the great majority, however brilliant they may be intellectually, are uniquely interested in getting on in the world. They may be eager enough to learn all the varieties of style and presentation and to distinguish between the logical and the illogical, but this is not because they want to write or speak with beauty or to express truth with clarity. Their aim is simply to win applause, recognition and, in the end, money. In education, just as in the law, the old aim of 'making men better' is no longer recognized.

Must we, I wonder, as we grow older, grow acquiescent to what we used to despise or deplore? Can we for ever, as it were, be fighting against the way of the world? For what wisdom have we got that can justify us in thinking that we are superior to others? Augustine tells me that he himself, with a nature so much finer and stronger than mine, often thinks along these lines. For if he could forget or at least thrust into the back of his mind that appetite and longing for wisdom and truth which have both inspired and tortured us for so long, then, it sometimes seems, he could be happy. Were he to set himself to it, by using and enjoying the talents which he possesses he could obtain in the end, and perhaps soon, some high position, as governor of a province, perhaps, or as an adviser to the emperor. And in such a post he would have not only honour and wealth but also the opportunity to be effective, to do good.

Often to me, too, such a solution as this seems not only sensible but modest. Why then is it that still from somewhere within me comes a strange note of warning, a conviction or something like a conviction that this good sense would be a betrayal of our youth, this modesty a mere surrender?

V

It is now the new year, and the other day I was told by one of my colleagues in the court that it will be a new year in a very special sense. Since then I have often heard this strange and to my mind unwarranted statement repeated. It seems to be the fashionable thing to say. No one, however, will say straight out exactly what he expects to happen and though there is certainly a general, if vague, feeling of elation among the worshippers of the old Gods, the Christians, who are, except among the aristocracy, greatly in the majority here, do not seem unduly disturbed. As usual they are more concerned with their own heresies than with anything else. And not even the most fanatical believers in the old religion would imagine that there is any likelihood of a return to the days when the Emperor Julius attempted with such little success to suppress the Christians and bring back the religion of the past.

Nevertheless there is a feeling that something or other in some way will be changed and this feeling seems to derive simply from the fact that Praetextatus is praetorian prefect and Symmachus prefect of the city. Both are known to be worshippers of the old Gods and Praetextatus is more generally admired and respected than anyone in Rome. Even the Christians admit his perfect integrity and some of them approve of his tolerance. It is certainly some time since so many and such important offices in Rome and Italy have been held by non-Christians, but I cannot see in this fact any evidence that the emperor and his advisers intend any great change. The appointments seem to have been made in the interests of efficiency and also, no doubt, with a view to securing the loyalty of the population of Rome; for the young Emperor Valentinian is still in a very insecure position. Beyond the Alps Maximus is in complete control and in Italy itself the emperor, or rather his mother, Justina, has alienated many of the orthodox Christians because of her ardent support of the heresy of the Arians who believe, so far as I can make out, that Jesus was not a god at all, or else was not fully divine in the sense that God the Father is divine. With some such a notion as this Praetextatus himself might well be in sympathy; it is also a view widely held throughout the East and in the army, expecially among the Gothic troops. To the orthodox however it is, of course, anathema and I have heard that in Milan relations between the powerful Bishop Ambrose and the Empress Justina are extremely strained. On the question of religious doctrine Ambrose will make no concessions at all. He had refused to recognize any Arian bishop in his diocese or to make available to Justina any church in the city for the use of her own sect. On the other hand he is wholly loyal to the young emperor himself and has refused, so it is said, to give any encouragement to Maximus whom he had denounced as a murderer and a usurper. One cannot help admiring both his courage and his consistency. He is inflexible in following what he believes to be right in theory and in practice; his ambition is not personal; and by all accounts he is remarkably considerate, gentle and eloquent in the expression even of those beliefs which he holds with the greatest conviction. I should very much like to listen to him speak. They say that even the largest church in Milan is scarcely big enough to contain all those who come to hear him.

It would seem however that, even though he is worshipped as a father by the people of Milan, he has, no doubt because of his doctrinal quarrel with the emperor's mother, less political influence than he used to have in the time of Gratian. I can scarcely believe that he would have approved of the appointment simultaneously to two such high offices of the known leaders of that part of the senate which opposes both the Christian religion itself and, in particular, its claim to be the only religion tolerated in the empire. No doubt he admires Symmachus for his eloquence and with Praetextatus he has much in common, being himself an aristocrat, an administrator, a scholar and a man of integrity. But from all I have heard of him it seems that, whatever his respect for the qualities of others, he would always put the interests of his Church (or, as I suppose he would say, his God) before everything else. He is in no sense a fanatic and yet his intransigence on certain points is absolute. As I say, I should like to know more about him.

Meanwhile in Rome, in spite of current gossip, I can really observe nothing new at all. No doubt there will be more deputations to the emperor with regard to the restoration of the statue of Victory to its time-honoured place in the senate-house; but does anyone mind very much about this except Symmachus and a few of his friends? No doubt that under Praetextatus government in general will be carried out with greater honesty and efficiency than has been known for some time; but there has been good government in Italy before now. We shall be turning, I think, to the past for some good things which have been lost, but these good things will be, as it were, excavated rather than reborn. What I, and I think many people, look for and do not find is a government that is alive and that will carry us into a future that is fresh and promising. As it is, the best that seems likely is a buttressing of ruins or an arrest of decay. There was something moving, but at the same time something pathetic, in the jubilation of the crowds on the day when Praetextatus appeared to take over his new office. Names from a dimly imagined past were constantly to be heard—Fabius, Scipio, Pompey, Caesar, Trajan—and it was as though people were attempting to convince themselves that something great and glorious, which, for no very good reason, they believed had existed once, was now miraculously coming into existence again. And yet all the time they were uneasily aware that they were in fact the same people as they were yesterday, reluctant to serve in the army, lacking conviction, interested chiefly in amusement, in personal ambition and in avoiding taxation.

However, though nothing, as it seems to me, has really changed, there is certainly something in the character and record of Praetextatus for which people can genuinely feel grateful. He is not a Scipio or a Caesar, nor would he pretend to be. And I think that characters of such force and grandeur, if they did exist, would be unable to display their qualities in the present age, an age in which much of the apparatus of government is purely mechanical and, from the emperor downwards, the greater a man is the more remote he is also from his fellow men. The popularity of Praetextatus does not spring from any belief that he either wishes or has the ability to introduce any great innovations in either peace or war. What people admire in him is stability rather than ambition. So in a sense what is expected of him is the exact opposite of what is being said. It is not the new that is desired, but a dignification of the old. The fine moral qualities of Praetextatus, his splendid bearing, his reasoned conservatism, his humanity combine to give the citizens of Rome the illusion that they themselves are better than they are. They are able somehow to believe that they indeed resemble those Romans of the past who, in the legions of Pompey or Caesar, once conquered the world, and this even though they must know in their hearts that they would go to any lengths to avoid any military service at all. It is as though they believe that so long as one man can be shown to be good, it follows that all men who applaud him are also good. Here, at least to a certain extent, the Christians seem to me to be more rational. They believe that Jesus is God and therefore perfectly good; then they are somehow able to believe that he is, or was, also a man and this, of course, must enable them to feel more intimately and closely connected with him than they could possibly feel with regard to Apollo, Ceres or Isis, who can be worshipped but scarcely loved. Yet the perfect goodness of their man-God does not necessarily give them illusions about themselves. To do them justice, they talk almost as much about their own sins as about the sins of others. They admit, as do the Manichaeans, what they describe as their 'fallen nature', and yet they are able to feel a kind of elation owing to this curious belief that their God has, in some incomprehensible way, shared their nature with them. Thus, if one could ignore the logical impossibility of a God being also a man, there would be something very attractive in this way of thought; for they are not wholly remote from their God as, it seems to me, even the greatest philosophers must be; nor are they irresponsible with regard to themselves, as must be all who extravagantly admire and positively identify themselves with a great man, whether it be a Caesar or a Praetextatus.

At least it may be said that, if one is going to identify oneself with and worship a human being, it is a healthier thing to entertain those feelings for a man like Praetextatus than for an emperor, a gladiator or a charioteer. Praetextatus is admired for good reasons, whereas the others have been worshipped and acclaimed often enough simply as incarnations of irresponsible power or of cruel or frivolous success. And perhaps what is really new in the situation is that for once a thoroughly good man has reached the very highest office. On this point all worshippers of the old Gods and most Christians can agree.

The great popularity of Praetextatus, then, is due simply to his own good qualities, has little or nothing to do with his religious beliefs and is certainly no indication that people are going to change their own. Symmachus, after all, has the same beliefs as Praetextatus, but he is admired only for his skill in rhetoric and only by a small circle. Praetextatus does seem in his own person to represent what are assumed to have been the virtues of the past, whereas all the skill and enthusiasm which Symmachus shows in re-introducing old rituals and old manners leave most people absolutely unmoved. Probably he won some temporary popularity by his action when, in a most elegant address, he congratulated the emperor on sending to Rome some Sarmatian captives to gratify the crowd in the arena by fighting either with themselves, with trained gladiators or with wild beasts. But this sort of popularity is a very different thing from that enjoyed by Praetextatus.

I myself have profited from my landlord's mistaken belief that I am more than a mere acquaintance of both Praetextatus and Symmachus. He has insisted on moving me into the best room in the house (not adding considerably to the rent) and nothing that I can say will convince him that my influence with these great men is quite negligible or that, even if it were not, I should not know how to employ it on his behalf. He is constantly urging me to call on one or other of these important people whom he likes to describe as my friends and, though I suppose I ought, since I have met them and since they have visited my father's house in Thagaste, to offer some expression of my congratulations, the effect of my landlord's importunity is to make me continue to put off what is, after all, a social duty. Yesterday, however, he did succeed in arousing my interest, even though what he proposes is absurd. He came into my room early in the morning, before I had got up, and without bothering to excuse himself, said in great excitement: 'You must go at once and see your friend Symmachus. You, with your influence, will be able to make the fortune of one who loves you.'

I imagined that by 'one who loves you' he meant himself and was prepared to be angry on all sorts of counts, but it soon appeared that he was speaking of Augustine. He had heard (and his information was, for once, correct) that the emperor (meaning the appropriate official) had entrusted Symmachus with the task of choosing in Rome a professor of rhetoric to hold a government appointment in that subject in Milan. What particularly impressed my landlord was that this professor, when appointed, would be provided out of public funds with a carriage and an escort to take him to Milan from Rome. And as he has often heard me talk of the great abilities of Augustine, he immediately concluded that a word from me would be sufficient to obtain this appointment for my friend.

While I was attempting to convince him that I was in fact a far too unimportant person to have any say in a matter of this sort, Augustine's Manichaean friend, Proculeius, arrived. He too had come to ask for my help, though in a more rational way. He told me that a number of the most distinguished members of the Manichaean community in Rome, personal friends of Symmachus, were strongly in favour of Augustine's candidature and were prepared to use their considerable influence on his behalf. The difficulty was, said Proculeius, that Augustine himself was showing reluctance in putting his name forward. He had said first that it would be dishonest of him to accept the help of the Manichaeans when he no longer believed in the truth of their doctrine. Proculeius had shown him that this scruple could be disregarded, since these influential Manichaeans were perfectly aware of Augustine's divergence from them, but were still anxious to support him, partly because of his known ability, partly because, even if he was no longer one of them, he was at least sympathetic to them; also the mere fact that he was not a Christian was, to their mind, an advantage and Symmachus, also, they thought, would feel in the same way. But Augustine was still undecided and now Proculeius had come to urge me to join in convincing him of the great prospects that were open to him. Few, if any, he said, among the younger professors in Rome had a reputation equal to Augustine's, and in an appointment of this kind it was likely that a young man would be sought for.

I found this news both exciting and disturbing. It was, of course, evident to me that the professorship in Milan was something which any ambitious man would wish to have. And I could see too that Proculeius was probably right in thinking that Augustine had a good chance of being appointed. But here I felt some kind of hesitation. For though I have always rejoiced at every success which my friend has had in his profession, I cannot help feeling that his own enjoyment of success is not as great as is my own. The days have long passed when we were both beside ourselves with joy whenever he won a poetry prize or a prize for declamation. Now both he and I feel that these honours, however deserved, are not quite what we want and even though we cannot define precisely what it is that we do want, the feeling persists. So I could well understand his reluctance to commit himself immediately even to a course where honour was assured and ambition might be gratified. Yet it was clear that by every standard except that of our own ill-defined uneasiness it was certainly an opportunity that ought to be grasped. My thoughts then became more selfish. I imagined with dismay what it would be like for me living in Rome if Augustine were away in Milan. This consideration did not occupy my mind for more than a moment. I saw almost instantly that, if he were to go away, I would follow him. I have enough experience of law now to be able to earn my living easily in any city large enough to require the services of lawyers and (though this consideration does not influence me at all) Milan, not Rome, is the centre of government; certainly my parents would be happy to think of me working there.

But I still do not know whether Augustine will decide to apply for the post or not. I went to see him, of course, later in the day and found him excited with the prospect but far from sure about what he should do. Somehow he feels reluctant to accept the help of his Manichaean friends, even though they have made it quite clear that they expect nothing for themselves from him, supposing he is selected for the job. He, I think, would like to show gratitude in a practical way, if he were in a position to do so, but knows that he is now so far from sharing their beliefs that he would find it impossible sincerely to encourage others to adopt them. I imagine that I was able to convince him that this scruple is unnecessary. These Manichaeans know him well, have no illusions about his views, and seem to be acting in a spirit of pure friendship. Indeed, now this is plain to him, their very disinterestedness makes him inclined to follow their advice, since to every expression of friendship he will always react with warmth. He is attracted also by the thought that his mother, who plans to arrive in the course of the next few months, would enjoy listening to and perhaps meeting the famous bishop Ambrose.

On the whole I think that what at present deters him from putting in his application is the feeling that, should he be accepted, he would have taken some irrevocable step in the direction of political ambition. Lucilla too seems to fear this, though she will say nothing to him to show her fear or to give him the impression that she is setting herself in the way of his advancement. But with me, when we had the opportunity of a few minutes' private conversation, she expressed herself clearly and very pathetically. She began by assuring me that she had never at any time done anything to impede him in his career and when I told her that I knew this perfectly well, she appeared grateful. She went on calmly and sadly to tell me what her fears were and, though I should have liked to have done so, I could not argue that they were unreasonable. For if Augustine does reach an important position and wants to rise still higher, he will be encouraged on all sides to marry a woman of rank and fortune. Lucilla's parents were slaves, so that it would be impossible for him to marry her, nor would any woman of good family marry him unless his connection with her were broken off. Without any question his mother would encourage the separation; in fact, as Lucilla said, speaking, for once, with bitterness, this would be just the opportunity for which she had long waited. 'And if it happens,' she went on, 'I shall go back to Africa and I shall never touch another man. I shall be unhappy and so will he be. But how can this be God's will?'

Her eyes were full of tears, but she spoke calmly. Indeed there was something scarcely natural in her calm and I could see that her restraint was a kind of agony. I was deeply moved by her words, and for many reasons. In the first place it had seemed to me inconceivable that so cruel a parting could ever happen. I have known Lucilla and Augustine from the very beginning of their connection together; I have watched their boy grow up and I have seen something of their happiness. There are times, I know, when Augustine is resentful of the very power and strength of his feeling for her, but the feeling exists, nor is it at all, as he sometimes seems to imply, a feeling in which nothing is present except sexuality. Certainly I have never imagined that that bond could be broken. But I realized as she spoke that what she was saying was true, and that what she feared was perfectly possible. I wondered whether it was pride or delicacy on her part that made her reluctant, as she evidently was, even to mention her fears to Augustine himself. But I soon saw that in any case she was right, for Augustine, so keen-sighted and penetrating in the affairs of others, would be incapable of admitting that there were any grounds at all for her apprehension. Nor would it do any good if I myself were to tell him that in my view everything that she feared was all too likely to take place. He would tell me, as he so often does, that I do not understand these things. Yet on this point I know that I see more clearly than he does.

When I came away, my impression was that in all probability Augustine will apply for the post, even though he has not yet definitely made up his mind. Proculeius feels as I do and is delighted. I wish that I could feel equally pleased.

VI

It is now eight days since we heard of the sudden death of Praetextatus. Even now and even in Rome, this city of distraction and noise where no single event seems to hold people's attention for more than an hour or two, there are still many to be seen in mourning clothes and one can still sense in ordinary conversation something of the general dismay and consternation of the days that immediately followed the news. Everyone agrees that never in memory and indeed seldom in history has there been so genuine and so widespread a feeling of loss and of deprivation. For there was nothing artificial about the demonstrations which took place. There was no ostentation in the preparations for the funeral made by his widow, Paulina, and Symmachus, who was thought likely to use the sad occasion for a display or for some exhibition of magnificence, did much less than was expected of him. Indeed he actually turned down a proposal by the great lady Coelia Concordia, the senior member of the college of Vestal Virgins, that statues of Praetextatus should be set up in the temples of the Gods. Symmachus' friends justify his conduct on the grounds that he was acting in accordance with strict republican tradition. Cato, they say, would never have tolerated any proposal that a man should be given honours that properly belong only to the Gods. But most people believe that he was really actuated by a mean-spirited jealousy, fearing that all expressions of the genuine admiration felt for Praetextatus would somehow diminish his own importance. In fact, of course, his failure to join publicly in the general mourning has made him much more unpopular than he was before. Indeed to me he seems to have acted ungenerously as a friend and ineptly as a politician. On the day following the funeral, for instance, he gave orders that the games in the circus were to be held as usual, no doubt imagining that he would be given credit for not depriving the people of their pleasures. But no one attended the games at all and Symmachus, who had intended to preside at them, is said to have left Rome in a hurry, fearing a popular demonstration against himself. That no such demonstration took place is in itself remarkable. It seems that the death of Praetextatus had filled the people with so deep a feeling of loss that until some days had passed no one could spare a thought, even of anger or of indignation, for Symmachus.

Since I am only a very remote acquaintance I did not visit Paulina's house until yesterday. I arrived among the last of the callers and expected that I should leave again at once after I had said my few words of sympathy and of condolence. I was surprised when Paulina detained me and then sat talking to me for some time after the rest of the visitors had left. In fact I am always surprised by Paulina's kindness to me.

She began by saying: ' I am glad you have come, Alypius, and I did not expect you to come in the first few days. So many of those who came then came with prepared speeches in their mouths, but with no real feeling in their hearts either for my husband or for me. Some, I suppose, were disappointed because they had hoped to gain something if my husband had lived. They may even have been angry with him for dying. '

I noticed that, though her words were bitter, there was no bitterness at all in the expression of her face. She seemed merely to be stating facts and stating them even with a kind of amusement. As it happened I had prepared some kind of a speech to make, but I saw now how unbecoming and unnecessary such artificiality would be. I told her that, whatever the true feelings of some of her visitors might have been, there was no doubt about the genuine sorrow that was felt by the ordinary and unimportant people in Rome.

'Yes,' she said, 'that is true. The common people are still capable of respecting goodness. Of course they are also capable of every kind of barbarity. They are like children, a strange mixture of purity and impurity. But they are seldom absolutely blind to what is greater than they are, not blind as the rich and the ambitious are. That is why our religions both nourish and are nourished by the poor and the simple. We should have no hope in this world or the next if our faith depended on the guidance of professional philosophers.'

She spoke, as always, simply and with dignity. Her face, though grave, was calm and was capable of expressing not only her natural kindness but also amusement and interest in others. There was no trace of the ravages of grief; yet I knew that she had loved her husband with all the devotion of a wife and all the confidence and sincerity of a friend. It seemed to me that she did indeed possess that hope and certainty of which she was speaking. And how, I wondered, would Augustine or I or Nebridius have behaved in comparable circumstances? If one of us were to die, the others would be heartbroken and inconsolable. We like to think of ourselves as philosophers, but it was true our philosophy could give us no confidence and no hope that our loss could even be made good. We never found, except for transitory moments, the happiness that we pursued and believed to exist; and even in these transitory moments our happiness, if we paused to think, would be soured and chilled by the reflection that it was insecurely based, accidental and inexplicable. Yet Paulina, even in the moment of her loss, was, if not happy, serene and mistress of herself, with hope, as she said, in this world and the next.

On every occasion when I have spoken with her she has seemed able somehow to read my thoughts. Now she said with a smile, 'Of course my husband was a philosopher too—like you, Alypius, and perhaps, if you will allow me to say it, even more learned. But that was not important.'

'He was also,' I said, 'a great man. He could look back on a long career in which he had filled every great office and acted well and honourably in every one of them. He had reason to be happy.'

As I spoke I realized that I was employing words and ideas which were wholly conventional. It was not like this that I really thought of Praetextatus and I was failing to say what I wanted to say.

Paulina smiled again and said: 'And do you think that that was important to him or me?'

'No,' I said. 'I was speaking foolishly. There was something more. I feel it, but I cannot find the words for it. Was it his goodness?'

'His goodness, certainly,' she said, 'but again there is something more than that. There can be no goodness without God. Even the Christians understand that, though not so clearly as the Platonists and not half so clearly as those who, rich or poor, strong or weak, have been purely united with God in the mysteries.'

Again I must have looked puzzled. I knew, of course, that both Praetextatus and his wife were sincere and devoted believers in their religion and that they attached particular importance to those elements in it which seemed to be private rather than public, though it is true, I think, that there is a feeling of community between all those who have been initiated into the mysteries of Demeter, of Isis, of Attis or of some other cult. It had been Praetextatus, indeed, who had been responsible for preserving the mysteries of Eleusis at the time when, after the death of Julian, they should, according to a strict interpretation of the edict of the Emperor Valentinian, have been suppressed along with all other 'nocturnal rites'.

I knew too that there is little or no truth in the common Christian view that these mysteries are established merely to throw a cloak of religion over orgies of sexuality or of drunkenness. In some cases, no doubt, these charges would be justified and similar charges made against the Christians by their opponents would be equally justified. Celebrations of some of their sacraments have often degenerated into drunken orgies and some of the feasts they hold in memory of the martyrs have been marked by every kind of licence. But these practices have always been condemned both by the Christian bishops and by the priests of older religions such as those of Isis or Demeter. Indeed, so far as real goodness and purity of life are concerned, I have met with no Christians whom I could admire more than Praetextatus and Paulina. But while I admire them, as indeed, I suppose, I admired that priest Jerome, what I cannot understand is how they are able to think as they do.

Now once more Paulina began to answer me even before I had begun to frame my question in my own mind. 'We have talked about this before,' she said, 'and I know that you cannot see now what is perfectly clear to me. I think you will see it one day and then you will be happier. As it is you are trying to find truth by means of logic. It is not there.'

My mind went back to that time in Africa when, soon after we had become acquainted with the Manichees, Augustine and I would often argue with Monnica about various articles in the Christian faith which seemed to us meaningless or contradictory. Unlike Paulina, Monnica was not good at following a reasoned argument. But she usually remained calm. She would keep on saying: 'All you are doing is to destroy, destroy, destroy. All these things you are saying mean nothing.' Then, as often as not, she would leave the room and, so Augustine tells me, she would spend hours in weeping and in praying for him.

It was easier to talk to Paulina than to Monnica. I said, 'You are thinking, perhaps, that all the criticisms I am making in my mind are destructive. That is true and I wish it were not so. But you would not have me force myself to believe in what, however I examine it, seems to me incredible.'

'Is there anything incredible,' she asked, 'in the existence of God?'

'No,' I said, 'but I cannot find God.'

'You will never do so,' she said, 'by any exercise of reason. You can only reason about objects of experience. So you must experience God before you reason about Him. Then you can reason as much as you like.'

'But how,' I asked, 'can I have this experience? What in fact I do experience are certain moments of beauty or of goodness. All around them, even intermingled with them, I find ugliness, cruelty, meanness and a kind of horror. No doubt if I were able to see only those moments of beauty I might be able to agree with Plato that they are an indication of some supreme beauty, something not in this world, which may be called God. But how can I isolate one portion of reality from the rest and refuse to recognize the existence of what conflicts with it?'

Paulina smiled again. I saw that, unlike Monnica, she was not in the least vexed by this kind of argument. She was indeed as unimpressed by what I was trying to say as Monnica might have been, but she was neither wounded by it nor perplexed. 'Does not Plato say also,' she went on, 'that in order to have the kind of vision which I see you want to have it is necessary for the eyesight to be purged and purified? Then you will not neglect anything of what you see now, or think you see. You will simply see it differently, you will know that all the time you were seeing something which you did not recognize, that everything always and everywhere is full of God.'

I thought of the many arguments Augustine and I had had with the Manichaeans and with ourselves; of how we had demonstrated to our own satisfaction that if, as is said, God is present as a substance permeating all nature then there must be more of God in an elephant than in a man. Somehow as I looked at Paulina's face, in its certainty, dignity and kindness, arguments of this kind began to seem to me trivial and perhaps pointless, even though I could detect no logical fallacy in them.

Now she spoke almost apologetically. 'Of course,' she said, 'I am not a philosopher like my husband is.'

I must have shown in my expression some sign of surprise, for now she laughed and touched me on the arm. 'Yes,' she said, '"is", not "was". Do you think I could be talking to you like this if I did not believe that he is alive and happy and that we shall soon be united again?'

Of course I had imagined that she, like the Christians and many others, would hold the belief that the soul continued to exist after death and that in the next life there would be rewards for the good and penalties for the wicked. But now I was ashamed to recognize that, while I had admitted that such a view could logically be held, I had never in fact believed that anyone could really hold it with any confidence. I had assumed, I suppose, though without realizing that I was doing so, that there must be a certain element of hypocrisy, however pardonable, in the attitudes of those who subscribed to this belief and who, in times of loss, undoubtedly derived comfort from it. Now I saw in Paulina no shadow of doubt, no hint of evasion or reservation. She believed exactly what she said. Had I, I wondered, misjudged others as I had been prepared to misjudge her? Was I so bound up with myself that I could not even imagine the possibility of other people thinking in a manner unlike my own?

I found myself struggling for words and Paulina, perhaps wishing to relieve my embarrassment, went on to show me some verses she had written which were to be inscribed on her husband's tomb. 'You must forgive my bad poetry,' she said, as I began to read them, 'but you may be interested in what I have tried to say.'

I found her modesty, whether true or false, human and

charming. In fact the versification was extremely elegant and indeed more than elegant. It had the weight and dignity of lines which are not only written well, but written from the heart. In subject matter the beginning of the poem was conventional enough. It was simply a recital of all the positions of honour, political and military, which, from his earliest age, Praetextatus had held. It was, of course, an impressive list and one which, so far as titular dignity is concerned, could only be paralleled by the epitaphs of heroes of the republic or of some of the greatest emperors. Then the poem, suddenly and simply, without changing its tone, began to surprise. After the long recital of honours came the words: 'But these are nothing.' I cannot precisely recall the words which followed, but they were to the effect that to the dead man all honours, all power and riches and ambition were transitory and fleeting things, that what supremely mattered to him was the purity of his heart in which he was able to honour the manifold majesty of God and through which he and his wife together knew all mysteries of heaven and earth. There was no trace of pride or of arrogance in the making of these claims. Again Paulina seemed to be writing simply and directly of what she knew to be true and she went on to express with the same sincerity her devotion and gratitude to her husband. There were words of love but none of lamentation. Through him and with him, she stated, she had been freed from the common and dreaded lot of death and neither he nor she had anything to fear. Was she not priestess of Cybele and Attis, Hecate and Demeter? And both her union with Praetextatus and her knowledge of heavenly things had been sanctified and confirmed by the red baptism of the blood of the bull of Mithra.

As I read the verses I was strangely and profoundly moved. It was not that before then I had been unaware of the sincerity of Paulina's and her husband's religious beliefs. I had often thought of it and had come close to envying them for possessing, at least, in their own minds, a certainty which had so long eluded Augustine and me. But now it seemed to me that I had been looking at this matter wholly from the outside, critically, in the manner of one who analyses a poem either in respect of its meaning or of its metrical qualities and, in doing so, is blind to the true poem which results from the combination of the two; for the values of the metrical sound throw light upon the sense and the meaning itself is something that could never be expressed in prose. So I began to see that the religion of Paulina and of Praetextatus was an experience rather than a way of thought or of behaviour. And it was an experience which I had never had during all that long time when we had been so earnestly engaged in philosophical and metaphysical discussion, checking one system against another and finding no satisfaction in any of them. Some views we had dismissed almost without consideration since they had seemed to be obviously and unquestionably mistaken. Among these was the notion that any wisdom or insight could come to a man who participated in the Mithraic rite of baptism, a mere drenching in the blood of a bull. And equally barbarous had seemed to us the Christian view that the divine spirit can be wholly incorporated in the body of a man.

Now I could see, and indeed I had always seen, that there was nothing at all barbarous about Paulina. There is no woman whom I admire and respect more. And yet I shrank from the imagination of her, carried away, no doubt, in a kind of ecstasy which to me was incomprehensible, and standing naked in a trench bathing in an animal's sticky blood descending on her from above. It occurred to me that I had often experienced the same reluctance of imagination when I had thought of what must have been the sexual experiences of my own parents or of Augustine and Lucilla. And I still feel that reluctance, even though I am now able to recall calmly and objectively (nor do I know quite how this has come about) every incident of the one experience of the same nature (if it can be said to be of the same nature) which I have enjoyed myself. It seems that there may be privacies or, as Paulina would say, mysteries which are not necessarily disgusting and of which I know too little.

I left her with the warmest feelings of affection and of gratitude. It is her goodness and kindness which stir my affection and I am grateful to her because she has shown me something of importance even though I do not know precisely what it is.

VII

Yesterday Augustine left Rome for Milan. I do not feel so lonely as I imagined I should, since now there seems so much to which I can look forward. In a few weeks' time I shall follow him to Milan myself and there, to our very great pleasure, we are to be joined by Nebridius. He had written both to me and to Augustine, saying that he had been missing us far too long and that he is determined to come to Italy for at least a year so that he can be with us again. He is rich enough, of course, to do as he wants and now he is even richer than before. For some years, partly from a sense of duty, partly because of his natural passion for efficiency, he has been devoting himself to the management of his large estate near Carthage. At first, he says, he found the work fascinating and took a kind of artistic pride in reorganizing the use of labour, in introducing new methods of cultivation, in estimating the demands of local and foreign markets and in all the activities which most great landowners leave, usually to their own loss, in the hands of others. His estate has always been a valuable one, but now, he tells us, it is worth rather more than twice what it was worth before he began to give it his full attention. Naturally his mother and sisters were pleased and he himself was flattered by the respect in which he was held by important people in the district and by senators in Carthage. All this time, as I know from his letters, he has continued to read and to study as we used to do together. He recognized the intellectual defects of Manichaeism even before Augustine did and, perhaps for that reason, has ceased to believe in the possibility of a science of astrology at a time when both Augustine and I, in our desire to find some sort of an intelligible correspondence between ourselves and the most remote objects in the universe, were inclined to think that there was something more than coincidence or just common sense in the predictions, so often verified, of the astrologers. And yet, though his very powerful and critical intellect has enabled him to avoid or to extricate himself quickly from some of the errors into which Augustine and I have fallen, he is painfully conscious that he has come no nearer than we have to the wisdom and certainty which we seek. He is now proposing a plan of life which I myself find extremely attractive, thought of course it will have to be discussed and, at least for the time being, I do not see how Augustine, who has just accepted this important post in Milan, could enter into it. Briefly, his idea is that a chosen group of us should put our property together into a common fund and should live as a community devoted only to the enjoyment of friendship and to the pursuit of wisdom. Each member would take his turn in administering the common property and in organizing meals, the employment of servants and other branches of economy. In this way we would be freed entirely from the cares, the wants and the ambitions which vex the lives of almost everyone in the world. We would be living the best life known to us and we would be only concerned to make this life better and happier every day. Nebridius says that this scheme originated with my rich kinsman, Romanianus, whose enthusiasm for it is such that he is determined to come to Italy himself very shortly and talk it over with us. Romanianus is older than any of us, but, though we began by treating him with the deference due to his rank and age, we now look upon him as a friend. His interest in Augustine began, as he has often told us, merely by way of doing what he conceived to be his public duty. For he is much the most important man in our area and has done more than anyone else to beautify Thagaste and to secure all available amenities for its citizens. He had heard from all sides reports of the unusual genius which Augustine had shown at school and when, after an unfortunate business transaction, Patricius found it impossible to go on paying for his son's further education in Carthage, it was Romanianus who insisted on providing the necessary money. Patricius, who always hated the idea of being in debt to anyone, was at first much opposed to the idea, but in the end was won over, partly by the determination of Monnica that her son should have every possible advantage in life, and partly by the charm and tact of Romanianus himself. As for Augustine, he is without any feeling of false pride and is never surprised when others behave to him with the generosity which he himself would show to them if he had the means to do so and if they needed it. He was unaffectedly grateful and has remained so. And before long gratitude blended with friendship. At first Romanianus must have looked upon the young man as a deserving protégé and may have invited him to his house rather out of kindness than from a desire for his company. He then became more and more attracted by the brilliance of his conversation and the charm of his manner which he had heard of but scarcely experienced before. Soon, rather to the amusement of my father, and others, he would be quoting almost every statement which Augustine made on literature or philosophy and speaking of him with the kind of awe usually to be found only in a young pupil for some distinguished teacher. He had allowed his own studies to lapse, but now with his enormous energy and enthusiasm he threw himself into every subject which Augustine was either teaching or learning. He put the education of his two sons into Augustine's hands and at the time when Monnica, shocked and saddened by her son's anti-Christian conversation, refused to live in his company, he welcomed him into his own house. It was not long before he too became a Manichaean. Indeed Augustine owes much of his popularity among the Manichaeans to the fact that it was he who converted to their beliefs such an important man as Romanianus. Augustine on his side has constantly sought the advice of the older man in all practical affairs and has regarded him after the death of Patricius as a father, though, it must be said, a much more intelligent and an even more indulgent one than Patricius was. He was in the habit of sharing all his ideas and all his plans with him. Only when he had decided to leave Africa and come to Rome did he keep the decision secret and he is now almost as ashamed of his secrecy on this occasion as he is of his desertion of Monnica. He knew, of course, that Romanianus would do everything to keep him in Africa and might well make use of an appeal to the gratitude which Augustine certainly owed him and to his duty to continue the supervision of the education of his sons. Augustine now blames himself bitterly for his cowardice in avoiding what would undoubtedly have been a painful interview. I fancy that his natural good breeding and kindness would have prevented him from doing so, if he had not been already worn out by the opposition between himself and his mother and was thus quite incapable of facing a situation in which he was bound to cause still more pain to a person whom he loved. In fact Romanianus has never written a word of reproach to him and this forbearance and generosity of his, while it has increased Augustine's esteem and affection for his friend, has made him feel all the more ashamed of his own conduct. He is now delighted at the prospect of seeing him again, almost as delighted as both he and I are at the coming of Nebridius.

He knows too, of course, how pleased and proud Romanianus will be when he hears of his important appointment in

Milan. That a native of Thagaste should win such distinction so young would be enough in itself to make Romanianus happy; but that this man should be Augustine, who owes so much to him and whom he loves so dearly, will almost overpower him with joy. I wish I could see him when he hears the news.

Augustine must also be pleased by the fact that without doubt he got this appointment on his merits. Of course in all public appointments influence counts and certainly those Manichaean friends of Symmachus who supported Augustine's application must have helped him. It is even possible that the decision to appoint him had been already made before the competition in speech and rhetoric was held in the presence of Symmachus and a certain number of the general public. Everyone agrees, however, that at this competition Augustine's performance was greatly superior to that of anyone else. There were the usual set speeches in which the aim is to impress the audience not only with the speaker's learning, eloquence and force of language but also with his manner of delivery. So far as learning and eloquence are concerned Augustine is and always has been outstanding; but he is often worried about his delivery, since his voice is not strong and certain passages of declamation are held to demand a volume and intensity of voice which he sometimes finds difficult to achieve. We are told that Cicero himself used to experience the same kind of difficulty and one would have thought that this fact in itself might have prevented Augustine from taking what he thinks to be his own disability so seriously. However, whenever he has to make a public appearance he is intensely nervous and, in spite of his repeated successes, is always afraid of failure. We, his friends, always know, of course, that he will do well, but we can never convince him of this. And on this occasion I have never known him to do better. The very restraint of his voice seemed to emphasize the brilliance and daring of his comparisons and the unexpectedness of his phrases. Even his competitors, some of whom I know to be very vain men, seemed to recognize his superiority and to join quite sincerely in the applause when Symmachus conferred the appointment on him.

After it was all over I went home with him. He was tired and, as always happens, genuinely surprised by his own success. This was not, I think, because he imagined that anyone had given a performance better than or equal to his own. Quite obviously no one had. It is rather the case that, undervaluing his own ability, he expects to be surpassed by others. So each success comes to him as something fresh and new, something also in which he associates his friends, enjoying their happiness more than the thought of his own achievement.

Lucilla, of course, knows him as well as I do and when we reached his rooms where she and the young boy, Adeodatus, were waiting for us, she could see immediately from his face what the result of the competition had been. It is impossible not to admire the simplicity and strength of her affection for him. I know her fears for the future and they must have been present to her mind as she threw her arms round his neck and congratulated him. Yet her congratulations were, I believe, perfectly sincere. She seems to be pleased with everything that pleases him. If he wants to be a great man, she is willing for him to be so, even though his greatness may weaken her own position with him and even though she knows what her own unhappiness would be if she were to be separated from him. She never shows him this knowledge of hers, with which I myself sympathize, and he does not appear to be at all conscious of it. All through that evening she behaved with the greatest gaiety and Augustine shared her mood and soon seemed to have thrown aside all the tiredness he had shown previously. Probably it was I who appeared the least cheerful member of the party, though I did my best to be as gay as the others, partly to please Augustine and partly, I think, to help Lucilla in what seemed to me a generous and pathetic deception both of Augustine and of herself.

So we made plans about how we would live together in Milan. We went through the names of various old friends of ours from Africa who were engaged there in the imperial service, either in the army or in other capacities. We looked forward with delight to the arrival of Nebridius and Romanianus, as we discussed their plan for a life in common, devoted to wisdom and to friendship. I could see that Lucilla was not greatly impressed by this plan and even when Augustine spoke enthusiastically of it, she was not willing to agree with him. 'What will happen to the women?' she asked simply.

This, in fact, was a question which had occurred to me also. For neither Lucilla herself nor the wives of Nebridius and Romanianus are fitted either by nature or training for philosophical studies. Also, whatever Lucilla might accept, I could not imagine the other wives as being willing to see their husbands devoting less and less attention to them and to the ordinary pleasures of society, which, on the whole, women seem to enjoy more than men. Moreover in all of these philosophical communities of which I have heard it seems to be assumed that abstinence from sex is, if not absolutely necessary, at least desirable and I think that of all the proposed members of the group, whether male or female, I am myself the only one who would readily accept this condition.

On this occasion Augustine, who was in very good spirits, brushed Lucilla's questions aside. He gave us an imposing list of great philosophers and spiritual teachers of the past who had been married or had lived in concubinage. I was somewhat surprised to find him citing among his examples the patriarchs of the Old Testament, the very people whom he had been in the habit of attacking for both moral and intellectual inconsistency. However, with this aspect of their conduct he appears satisfied. Both Lucilla and I found his enthusiasm amusing and again I began to wonder whether, since my friend evidently found the pleasures of sex so necessary and delightful, I myself ought not to acquire a wife, or at least a mistress, so that I might have an opportunity of discovering whether or not I was missing something of the greatest value. One thing which deters me is that, whenever I mention this idea to Augustine himself, he earnestly opposes it and begins to congratulate me on my present state. Here again his attitude is surely strangely inconsistent.

I think that Lucilla enjoyed the conversation most when we were talking about our proposed philosophical community. Anything that gives pleasure to Augustine, so long as it does not threaten her, pleases her too and Augustine, relaxed after the exertions of the day, was now enjoying in imagination the communal life with his friends almost as much as if it were already a reality. She enjoyed, too, everything we were able to tell her about Milan, though it is true that we know only very little about it ourselves. In all this talk she joined eagerly. It was only when Augustine began to speak of his mother and to assure Lucilla that life with her would no longer be difficult, as it had been, but would be a continual source of pleasure to them all that she began to lose her gaiety and to answer his questions automatically or dispiritedly. I was surprised that though her embarrassment on this subject was, however much she tried to conceal it, evident to me, Augustine seemed wholly unaware of it. It would be truer to say, I think, that this insensitiveness of his comes from an excess than from a lack of affection. He cannot imagine, in spite of his experience, that those whom he loves and who love him will not love each other. Or, if he does imagine this, he refuses to admit it as a possibility. And it may be that he speaks with such apparent assurance because he is determined to believe something that he suspects may not be true.

His mother is expected to arrive in Milan at about the same time as I do. I wish I could believe that Augustine's confidence in the future relationships of his family was justified. It is a situation where I want to be of help, and yet I can think of nothing valuable which I could do or say. As it happened I found myself constantly leading the conversation away from Monnica and back to other subjects such as Nebridius or the speeches made that morning. So on the whole our evening was a gay one and Lucilla appeared grateful to me. But I had done nothing of real value.

VIII

I have had to stay in Rome for a longer time than I expected and it is now nearly three months since Augustine left. However, I shall be setting out for Milan in few days' time. There will be no difficulty, I am told, in finding work there and my parents are, on the whole, pleased that I am going, particularly as I, with the help of Romanianus, may be able to bring to the notice of the appropriate authorities the extortionate behaviour of some of the tax-collectors in our district in Africa.

Augustine has written to me several times and at length. Much of what he has written concerns his impressions of Bishop Ambrose. This man is, I suppose, the most powerful of all the Christian bishops and it seems that in Milan he has at least as great a reputation as Praetextatus had in Rome, being admired both by his coreligionists and by others. Moreover, like Praetextatus, he evidently deserves it. He is a man of good family, a fine scholar and an expert administrator. His father was praetorian prefect of Gaul and Ambrose himself might have been expected to rise to some high office in the state, either military or civil. Instead, at a very early age (he was, Augustine tells me, only thirty-four) he was made bishop by popular acclamation. This is a proceeding which is common in the Christian churches and the motives for this method of election are various. Indeed 'election' is scarcely the word to use; it is often, as I have seen in Africa, more like compulsion. There are times, certainly, when a man known for his sanctity or ability is encouraged, or forced, to take office. At other times, however, what chiefly interests the Christian mob, who can behave with extreme violence, is to secure for their own church a man who is simply rich or else famous for learning so that they may benefit both from his riches and from his reputation. Ambrose, no doubt, possessed every quality that could be desired and he is not alone among Christian bishops in having been elevated to his position before he had even been baptized.

Augustine is always grateful, indeed almost extravagantly grateful, for any kindness or courtesy that is shown to him. He was greatly impressed by the welcome which he received from Ambrose when he arrived in Milan, though of course this welcome was no more than might be expected from a man of breeding who is also a scholar. Since then he has been, he tells me, on every possible occasion to hear Ambrose preach. At first he went out of curiosity, in order to compare his style with that of other speakers whom he has heard and to estimate whether his great reputation is deserved or not. He found his language less varied, less fanciful and perhaps less charming than the language of Faustus whom he had listened to in Carthage; but on the other hand there was a force, a sincerity and a simplicity which Faustus lacked. He began, he says, by listening to him in a purely critical way, judging him by the standards which would apply to any speaker; soon, however, he became impressed by what Ambrose was actually saying and by a quality of intellectual honesty which he had never found even in the best speakers among the Manichees. And from this respect for his eloquence and for his character he was quickly led on, it seems, to the conviction that much of what Ambrose was saying was true. In particular there were passages of the Old Testament which were explained in a way that was not only new but which made perfectly good sense. Some of these passages were ones at which we had often laughed because of what seemed to us their obscurity or their incoherence. Augustine now tells me that a wise man would laugh not at them but at us for our inability to see the profound symbolic meaning of stories or expressions which we looked at so carelessly as scarcely even to perceive the surface. Now, he says, he spends whatever time he can spare from his work in reading the Bible and he has become convinced that it is, at least in some sense, divinely inspired. It amazed me to find him writing with the utmost enthusiasm about its style. since we have so often contrasted the Bible unfavourably, both as regards style and matter, with the works of Plato or of Cicero. In particular we objected to the childish simplicity of its language and syntax, but it seems that if it is true that, as the Christians say, this book is the word of God, may we not assume that God would so instruct those who were speaking for Him (Moses, the prophets and the rest) that this word should be accessible to all the world? And this, in fact, is just what we find. Whereas only people of some education can make much out of Plato or Cicero, a child or an illiterate can enjoy and to some extent understand the words of the Bible. And in these words are to be found, too, suggestions so profound that they will illuminate the minds of the most intelligent. It is, he says, a style absolutely unlike anything else—a combination of simplicity and complexity—and on the evidence of style alone it is not an unreasonable assumption that all that the Christians say of this book may be true.

Having reached this conclusion, Augustine is, of course, following it up with his usual energy. Up to this time, while entirely dissatisfied with the specific doctrines of the Manichees, he assented to much of their criticism of the Christians, and probably would have admitted that, though they could not provide him with truth, they were at least no more wrong than any other sect. Now, however, that he has decided that even their critical attitudes are mistaken he finds nothing to be said for them at all. He has actually become a Christian catechumen, thus involving him at least to some extent in the Christian community. It is characteristic of him to take this step so quickly. He feels, I imagine, that he must in some way indicate (rather to himself than to others) that he has finally cut himself off from all that Manichaean faith which for so long he has followed with varying degrees of enthusiasm and dissatisfaction. And it is equally characteristic of him that, though partially a member of the Christian Church, he will not go on, impulsive as he is, to take the irrevocable step of baptism. I fancy that he may well desire to take this step, since it is his nature to seek the irrevocable. He knows, too, that all through his life his mother has prayed for nothing more earnestly than to see him a baptized Catholic. To give her the happiness for which she had longed for so many years and at the same time to find peace for himself must be therefore a powerful inducement to him. Yet I know too that no consideration either for her happiness or for his own peace of mind could ever make him accept as true what he does not plainly see to be so. Indeed his mind could not find rest in something of which he could say no more than that it seems the most likely solution, nor, in his view, could her happiness be anything but illusory or even hypocritical unless he were able to accept her faith as wholeheartedly as she herself does. I wonder, as I know that he has often wondered, whether such total acceptance is possible for any except the simple-minded. However, possible or not, this is what he demands.

I think too that, altogether apart from his intellectual integrity, there is another consideration which deters him. This concerns the nature and strength of his feelings towards Lucilla. He has often spoken to me on this subject and he has often recurred to it in the letters I have received recently. As for me, I can easily understand his intellectual reluctance to accept a faith that cannot be demonstrated. I should feel, though perhaps less strongly, the same reluctance myself.

But I confess that I am puzzled by his attitude with regard to his sexual life. I know, of course, that among baptized Christians all sexual relationships outside marriage are considered wrong, and though this is a rule that is frequently broken Augustine is not, of course, a man who would find an excuse for himself in the delinquencies of others, however common they might be. It would seem quite natural, then, that considering the strengths of his attachment to Lucilla, he would shrink from adopting a course which would in the end demand his separation from her—something which would cause infinite pain both to her and to himself. But this is not precisely the way in which he feels. Or rather, though he does feel this, and feel it very strongly, he is also distraught by other emotions of a very different kind. It is a kind of ambivalence which I find difficult to understand. His love for Lucilla is both violent and tender, and yet, while fully conscious of this fact, there are times when he seems to resent its violence and to deplore its tenderness. It is as though he wants both to enjoy it fully and to get rid of it entirely. He never shows any of this resentment to Lucilla herself; he would not willingly do anything to hurt her and indeed the kind of resentment that he feels is not directed against her at all. It is directed against himself and, in a sense, against what seems to be the nature of things. Sometimes he will express himself by saying that it is a shame for a man to be a slave to passions that he cannot control. Such a sentiment is, of course, a commonplace amongst moral philosophers, particularly among the Stoics whose ideal of complete self-mastery and self-sufficiency, while admirable in some ways, seems to me often to spring from a kind of arrogant egotism, as though man's supreme good was to contemplate his own goodness and integrity. But in Augustine, of course, nothing of this kind of pride is to be found. He would neither claim to be nor want to be self-sufficient and, independent as he is in his thought, he is happy to be in many ways dependent on others. It is only, I should say, in the matter of sex that he

186

resents this dependence. He resents the fact and yet he loves the person who to him is the embodiment of this fact. Obviously the two attitudes are inconsistent, yet, since both of them are his, he will find himself arguing now for one attitude and now for the other and, however lucid his arguments may be, he must know that if one of them is valid the other cannot possibly be so.

I must own that my one experience of sex left me in a state of mind which may have certain similarities with that of Augustine. And yet the differences between my experience and his must be so great that I hesitate to make the comparison. It is true, however, that in that brothel in Madaura I did feel, during the act of sex itself and immediately afterwards, emotions which were not only violent but inexpressibly tender, satisfying and, in a very real sense, good. They were, of course, except from the most purely physical point of view, irrational and misplaced; but still they existed. Then what seemed to me the bestial and lascivious conduct of my friend and of the girl herself filled me with a shame and a disgust just as powerful as had been those feelings of trust, confidence, gentleness and peace which I had experienced a moment before.

Obviously the relationship between Augustine and Lucilla is of a very different nature from that experience of mine, which, except in a special sense, can scarcely be called a relationship at all. I never even knew the girl's name and could form only the remotest notion of what her character might be. Everything was over in a moment and, though I certainly experienced affection, I can see no rational grounds for having done so. But Augustine and Lucilla have known each other for years; they have had a child together; they have the sympathy that comes of long intimacy, and though Lucilla may not be able to follow the movements of Augustine's mind as well as Nebridius or I can, she understands his moods and the expressions of his face at least as well as we do and so may be described as a friend as well as a mistress. Nevertheless

187

there is, of course, in this relationship an element of physical passion which is not present in the pure friendship of man for man, and it is this element which first brought them together and which, more than all else, still keeps them bound to each other. Even my own brief and unworthy experience of this passion had taught me, now that I am able to look back on it clearly, that in the act of sex itself there can be great good. I wonder, however, whether there may not be always and of necessity associated with it something also of bestiality and of shame. Is there not something ironical in the fact that the sexual act must be performed by means of organs normally used for the process of excretion? Moreover, except among the most depraved, this is an act to be done in secret, whereas the noblest activities of man can be performed openly and indeed often demand the witness and approbation of others.

Among the Christians it is, I think, held that the most desirable thing of all is to live a virgin life. Yet the Christians, unlike the Manichees, do admit the undesirability of the extinction of the whole human race. Also they are realistic enough the see that, however desirable a life of virginity may be, in fact the passions of most men and women are far too strong to be able to accept such a rule. They therefore recommend that the act of sex should only be performed for the express and deliberate purpose of bearing children and should be dissociated from any feelings of sensuality. This may seem intellectually to be a neat solution. In fact, however, if these sensual passions which they deplore were not, at least to some extent, aroused the man would be unable and the woman unwilling to perform the act at all.

I am almost inclined to believe that this sexual impulse is so contradictory in itself that no very rigid rules at all can be laid down either for its expression or for its control. A good man will be attracted by what is beautiful and repelled by what is bestial. But what is he to do when the peace and joy of an angel can only be secured by performing the physical motions of a dog or a bull? It seems to me that the rigid distinction, made first, I suppose, by Pythagoras, between the body and the soul is not entirely valid for human beings who, after all, are not so constituted that they can appreciate a work of beauty without eyes or ears. And just as the pure pleasure of friendship can be more deeply felt when one is actually able to see and hear one's friends, so this other pleasure of sexual intercourse, more gross, but also, in its own way, more intense, demands in the nature of things (which we did not determine) the co-operation of other physical organs which, unlike the eyes and the ears, are called, both in Greek and Latin, 'parts of shame'. It may be, therefore, that unless we accept this condition for what it is, we shall never be able to understand it or to profit by it. Both the beauty and the bestiality are there and cannot be denied, and if we attempt to suppress or to exaggerate one or other of the two elements, we shall be blinding ourselves to what exists.

Often when I have been thinking along these lines it has seemed to me that it would be good if I, too, were to take a mistress or to get married. I am not held back from this course by lack of money, good looks or vigour—only by a certain timidity, and this, I think, I should quite quickly overcome. I should like to have children and I should like sincerely and freely to enjoy pleasures which I have only tasted in a dubious and furtive manner. But whenever I mention these ideas to Augustine, he will implore me to put them out of my head and will assure me that I do not realize how happy I am in my present state—and this in spite of the fact that I am perfectly conscious that I am not happy, whereas if what he enjoys is not happiness it is difficult to see why it is that he cannot bear to be apart from Lucilla for more than a day on end. Yet happy as I believe him to be, he is, it seems, ashamed of this happiness and when I suggest to him that it may be possible for love wholly to overcome shame, he will tell me that, though this may indeed sometimes and momentarily appear to be the case, the fact is far different. I remember that, before he left Rome, I spoke to him again and at some length about that experience of mine in Madaura. He listened to me affectionately and then asked me to look deeply into my own mind and to consider whether, in a sense, it were not true that, beautiful as for a time my own feelings had been, I also felt not only disgust but a kind of fascination for the subsequent behaviour of my uncouth friend. Could it not be said that in this sense my friend and I represented two facets of a single personality?

I saw what he meant, but still cannot assent to this analysis. I am too conscious of the real differences in taste and in intelligence between that friend of mine and myself. But am I here imagining for myself a superiority that does not exist or, if it does, only exists in a superficial way? Augustine has not only a mind that is more powerful than my own, but also a kind of piercing sympathy which can reach behind the notions that, often in self-protection, we hold about ourselves. I told him, I remember, that if I attempted to put before my mind's eye himself and Lucilla in the place of that girl and that Priapus figure, I should find the operation impossible. He replied gravely and sadly that he himself would find no difficulty whatever in doing so. 'Undoubtedly,' he went on, 'there can be beauty and even a kind of innocence in this kind of love. The poets may exaggerate, but they do not invent. Among young lovers we will find a tremulous and touching kind of excitement, a hesitancy and an urgency at once, a desire to give and to trust as well as to have and to hold. The first embraces are like the opening up of a new and splendid world, and the delighted mind is startled and amazed by the body's delight. They believe that each is for each for ever and that there is nothing else, or nothing else of such importance. These feelings are genuine and they have too the mark of generosity, for in their purity there is very little of selfishness. It may even seem to them noble (and in a sense it is) that they are in the hands of a power greater than themselves, the universal force that leads all animated creation—

dogs, horses, lions, insects and flowers—into the necessity of desire, and they may regard themselves as ministers rather than as victims of this power.'

As I listened to him I felt that I understood his words. This, it seemed to me, was what I too desired. Was not this the tangible reality which lay behind so much of beauty? Were we not born for this, and was not I, in my youth, neglecting or avoiding my birthright?

Augustine noticed my look of enthusiasm. He himself had been speaking with a kind of fervour, but now he smiled sadly at me and went on rather more calmly and also with some diffidence, I thought. 'Of course all this is true,' he said, 'and one does not need the poets to tell one so. Nor does one need the witness of the poets to discover that these feelings are of necessity transient, and that the universal power that lies behind them can be, and in the end almost always is, disastrous and destructive of the very beauty into which at first it leads the way. We are indeed victims and not ministers, for this is not a power that we can worship. It is stronger than we are, certainly, but it is also inhuman. It forces us to copulation and, to do so, must adapt itself to, or make use of, elements in our human nature—instincts of tenderness, of unselfishness, of wonder and of worship—which in themselves have nothing whatever to do with this act. But once the act is performed and is enjoyed, this force, this "divine power", as it is incorrectly called (for what is divine must be not only stronger but higher than what is human), has achieved its object. And now the act of copulation, from which at the beginning, perhaps, we shrank or towards which we looked with the eagerness or the wonder that is provoked by the unknown, has become something familiar and necessary. It changes from an adventure to a habit. True that the act itself demands excitement and that what is wholly and entirely habitual is not exciting to the mind. From this act, however, the body can still drag excitement when the mind is already tired of it and disgusted with it. We actually can find an added pleasure in an increasing beastliness; the collapse of reason, the eclipse of all ideas of honour or of beauty, becomes the most agreeable of sensations. Each body becomes to the other an instrument for its own pleasure. Distinctions of beauty, kindness, intelligence cease to exist as we feverishly scratch the sores of our lust, forcing ourselves to a consummation of repetitive pleasures that have lost all wonder, all joy and all humanity. Now we cannot even claim for ourselves the innocence of beasts carried away by a universal force which, however inhuman, is at least natural. Indeed we delude ourselves if we imagine that we can ever abolish our own reason. We can only debase it, as we do in our bestial transports which, however frenzied, are still artificial, since we know perfectly well from memory and imagination what it is which we seek. This lust is conscious, premeditated and self-imposed. If in the course of its operation we seek also the pleasure of another, it is only in order to increase our own pleasure and when it is all over, though we may feel that both our bodies and our minds have been debased, we know that before many hours we shall be seeking precisely the same thing again. It may be this thought that prevents us from being wholly disgusted with each other. We are accomplices in debasement and may not even reflect on what we have done until soon the occasion arises for doing the same things again.'

His pain and his dissatisfaction were so evident in both his words and manner that I felt distressed for him and, though I should have liked to have questioned him further, I refrained from doing so. There is no doubt whatever that he meant what he said, but still what he had said had not satisfied me. Not that I thought he was deceiving himself. He is less prone to self-deception than any man I know. And yet this truth which he was certainly expressing did not seem to me to be the whole truth. He is apt to generalize from his own particular experiences and he recalls these experiences with an amazing accuracy and insight. But he is also apt, I think, to isolate and magnify, as it might be through a glass, one particular element in his experience and from this magnification to produce a general picture which may fail to take account of other elements to which he is not immediately directing his attention. I can well believe, for instance, that the sexual act, when frequently indulged in by the same two people, may, through familiarity, become perfunctory, a need of the body rather than an experience in which the whole personality is involved. This, indeed, is a commonplace in the poets, and what is remarkable in Augustine's treatment of this condition is not that he says anything new but that he speaks of what is known with a peculiar intensity and almost a savagery of resentment. Moreover he leaves much out of account. It seems to me that if this description of jaded and mechanical love were really true in respect of himself and of Lucilla, he would by this time have become tired of her and would be looking for another mistress. But this is certainly not the case. It is quite evident that he loves her as much as he ever did and that he loves her with a tenderness and a consideration which are quite incompatible with those feelings of resentment and disgust which, if they do exist, are by no means the whole of what exists in this relationship.

Here, as in so much else, it seems to me that he cannot bear to rest in anything less good than perfection. When he speaks as I have just described he reminds me of the monk Jerome whose language is perhaps even more savage than that of Augustine but who, like him, can feel and express an almost overpowering tenderness. His passion for virginity is something more than can be explained by a zeal for abnegation or a delight (often in itself sensual) in asceticism. To him virginity is good and beautiful in itself and not for the sacrifice which it entails. It is not a deprivation but a dignification of life.

I should have liked to have met Jerome again, but he has recently left Rome and gone, so they say, to Jerusalem. He was accompanied by several of those noble Roman ladies who have pledged themselves to the virgin life and who propose to form under his guidance a community devoted to prayer and to the care of the poor and sick. It seems that Jerome himself was fortunate to get away from Rome in safety, for just before he left it became known that the beautiful young girl Blaesilla, whom I met, or rather exchanged a few words with, had died and it was generally assumed that her death had been caused by the fasting and the austerities to which she had been subjected in the name of religion and by the advice or compulsion of Jerome. There was a day of rioting and the streets were full of disorderly mobs of men and women shouting out 'The monks to the Tiber!' and searching, in the first place, for Jerome himself. Before order was restored many monks had in fact been thrown into the river, and it is said that a few were drowned. Others were beaten or stoned. And it is significant that this was not a riot directed against the Christians (many in the mob were Christians themselves). Nor could anyone in his right mind have imagined that Jerome had been guilty of any deliberate cruelty. What chiefly inflamed their minds was the thought of a young, beautiful and noble girl having been persuaded to reject marriage and all the ordinary pleasures which are sought after by others. It was as though their own pleasures were being condemned and many in the mob, particularly the women, evidently regarded their savagery as something virtuous—could justify their evil passion for persecution and cruelty by imagining that they were vindicating what was natural and normal. And though, of course, one cannot fail to be disgusted by the brutality of crowds who, when stirred up in this way, become inhuman and insensitive, one cannot say that the underlying causes of riots are always unworthy of respect.

It is certainly possible to feel that the doctrines of Jerome tend to undermine the whole fabric of society and indeed this argument was constantly used until quite recently against the Christians as a whole. The emperors who not so long ago were attempting, by persecution of one kind or another, to repress or destroy this religion were not acting irresponsibly or out of cruelty. They believed (and there seems justification for the belief) that this faith was setting up a different order from that of the state, with different rules and with different loyalties. For while many philosophers have deplored the world in which we live, the Christians seemed to be denying it entirely or positively looking forward to what they regarded as its imminent destruction.

Now the Christians are firmly established and many of them show a desire to persecute others in their turn. Their religion is part of the fabric of the empire and they are showing less and less conviction in either the likelihood or the desirability of an approaching end to the world. Their accredited leaders are statesman rather than missionaries or revolutionaries. Yet while in practice they are a part, and a very important part, of the state, they still in theory regard themselves as above it and outside it. They will not only claim for themselves a special relationship with God, but clearly consider that those who do not agree with every word of their dogma can have no relationship with God whatsoever. So, while they have gained power and perhaps deserved to do so, they retain the exclusiveness which made them hated when they were in a minority. And men, though willing enough to admire the distinction of heroes or of saints, still like to think that the objects of their admiration belong at least to the same species as themselves. They resent what seems to them inhuman. And, or so it seems to me, it is by no means certain that this resentment is unjustified. Ought we not to cultivate and to improve our own natures and the world about us rather than to deny them all together, as Jerome sometimes appears to be doing?

I wonder what Augustine would think of this long and, as usual, inconclusive dialogue with myself. No doubt he would find flaws in my argument, but he might also see that the whole argument springs from my anxiety about himself. I cannot bear to see him in pain and I cannot bear the thought of him inflicting more pain, for however good reasons, on both Lucilla and himself.

part three

I

It is nearly two months since I arrived in Milan. If up to now I have made no attempt to write down my impressions, this is not only because I have been busy but also because my impressions have been so various and so contradictory.

At first what was uppermost in my mind was simply the pleasure of being once again in the company of my friends, and the excitement of seeing them and hearing of what they had been thinking or doing seemed to blend with the excitement of finding my way about this great imperial city, of visiting the churches and admiring the new buildings and the splendid processions of troops who are far more numerous here than in Rome. The whole place indeed seems to be more alive than Rome is and at first I found my friends, too, more vigorous, more interested in the present and the future than I had ever known them. I began to feel as though I had been buried in Rome and as though that city herself was a symbol rather than a reality, a splendid mausoleum for what had once been powerful and alive. It was here in Milan that the emperor's court and the vast machinery of government were concentrated. Around us were the most fertile plains and the most vigorous peoples of Italy. This was the country of Catullus and Virgil, of Caesar's legions, and beyond the plain were the gigantic Alps, the barrier of Italy and the road to Gaul, to Germany and to Britain. There was a kind of perennial challenge in the air and this sense of challenge was intensified by the fact, generally acknowledged here but in Rome scarcely even a topic of conversation, that behind the Alps Maximus was already massing his armies so that Milan, Italy and Rome herself, whether she was aware of it or not, were under the constant threat of invasion. Here one could believe that activity, even if not precisely understood, was meaningful and that ambition might be natural.

Nebridius, who had arrived some weeks before me, fully shared in my excitement, and so did Augustine, though in a somewhat different way. I thought that Nebridius had grown thinner and more thoughtful than he had been, but soon found that he was still exactly the friend I had known. Though he had professed an utter disillusionment with politics, now that he was close to a hostile frontier he showed the keenest interest in everything that was, or might be, going on in the councils of state or in the planning of the generals. Yet, interested as he was in political and military events and possibilities, he was still as devoted to philosophy, still as ardent in the search for faith as he had been in Carthage. I found that he, like Augustine but more slowly and deliberately, seemed to be turning in the direction of the faith of the Christians. He told me that he had found more to stimulate and to exercise his mind in Milan than he had ever found in Africa. He too was impressed by Ambrose, admiring him both for his eloquence and sincerity and for his courage in refusing to make any kind of concession to the Empress Justina with regard to her mode of worship. In the past I myself had often laughed at and occasionally been shocked by the peculiar insistence shown by the Christians on what seemed to me small and unimportant points of dogma; but now after listening two or three times to Ambrose's careful exposition of what is known as the Arian heresy, I can see that it is of real importance to the Christians to have this and other articles of their faith rigorously and exactly defined. Neither Nebridius nor Augustine nor I would pretend to know precisely what the Christians mean by their doctrine of the Trinity, but I can see that it is an important belief and there are moments when I do seem to come near to some kind of understanding of it. And it is clear that the view of the Trinity held by the Catholics is quite incompatible with that held by the Arians. Moreover, as Nebridius rightly points out, if the Christian religion merely puts forward the belief in a supreme God and in a prophet, divinely inspired, who can serve as a link between mortals and divinity, then there is little to distinguish Christianity from four or five other religions and there could be no justification for the Christian claim that no religion other than their own can be true. This is certainly a claim that is made by Ambrose most eloquently and the arguments which he puts forward in its support undoubtedly command respect; though neither Nebridius nor I is as convinced by them as Augustine who, as it seems to us, having found himself mistaken in some of the criticisms which he used to bring against the Christians, is now almost ready to believe that he was mistaken in all of them. Augustine has always been influenced by his affections as well as by his reason and he is unhappy when affection and reason do not point in the same direction. He would always have liked, for instance, to hold the same faith as his mother holds, but he can neither believe nor pretend to believe what seems to him untrue and Monnica, of course, lacks the intellectual equipment even to understand, let alone to confute, his arguments. But now in Ambrose he has found a man who commands his intellectual respect as well as his affection. And, or so it seems to me and to Nebridius, he is somewhat too apt to believe that a man of such nobility of character and so great an intellectual integrity must know the answer to every question.

He and Nebridius have been studying with fresh interest the works of the Neo-Platonists and Augustine claims to find in these works much that corresponds with the doctrines of the Christians. I agree that there are indeed certain similarities. Much of the beginning of the Gospel of St John, for instance, might have been written by a Neo-Platonist. I agree too that there is a strange and visionary beauty, something that deserves the name of religion as well as of philosophy, in the writings of Plotinus and his followers. But the argument still remains for the most part abstract. There is no mention of a God, or any aspect of God, who can remain God and still suffer as men do, nor can I see how such a conception can possibly be arrived at along the lines of Neo-Platonic argument. Augustine used to hold the same view and in fact used to admire the Neo-Platonic theory for a kind of intellectual consistency which could not be found, he used to say, in Christianity. Now, however, he seems to regard this very consistency as a defect. 'Everything is there,' he said to me the other day, 'except for one thing, and that is the most important thing of all.' And when I asked him what this one thing was, he replied, 'Humility in the knowledge of Jesus Christ.'

He saw that I was surprised by his words and added quickly, 'Don't think that I claim this humility and this knowledge. But I can see that I am too proud in my own conceit and that my pride is holding me back from where I want to be. There are moments when I am almost there. I am on the very point of surrendering myself, of abasing myself so that I shall rise; I feel the sweetness of it; I smell the fragrance; I am trembling towards the embrace and satisfaction of submission. But then all the past and the present come swarming round me like flies that shut off the light of the sun. Ambition, money, work, flesh drag me backwards and I fall away from my delight.'

He does not often speak like this, but when he does, he speaks with an extraordinary intensity and almost a desperation. I think sometimes that he has changed enormously during the last few months; but then I see that he has not changed at all. There is nothing in him that was not there before; all that has happened is an intensification of some inner struggle in which, maybe, he has been involved since childhood. I pray that this struggle may be resolved before it tears him in pieces. Altogether his nature is more intense than mine or that of Nebridius. We too feel dissatisfaction, but Augustine's feeling is far stronger than this. It is real pain. Or it is like a raging hunger for something of which he has smelt the savour, but has not quite reached; whereas we, still hungry, sniff the air merely and have no inkling of what the food might be for which we seek.

These moments, however, during which he is so acutely conscious of his pain, are not very frequent. For much of the time he appears to be content, and sometimes even happy, in his work. He has more to do than he had in Rome and, as might be expected, he does it very well. And he is appreciated not only by his pupils but by many of the most eminent literary men in Milan. It seems to me likely that before very long he will be offered some other important post in the imperial service, but I would still hesitate to guess whether he would accept such an appointment or not. He is certainly not without ambition and with much of his work he appears satisfied. There are other aspects of it, however, which displease and disgust him. The other day, for instance, Nebridius and I happened to be walking back with him from the theatre where, on the occasion of the young emperor's birthday, he had just delivered an official speech of congratulations and eulogy. The speech had been a model of its kind—gracefully learned, patriotic and complimentary. As convention demanded, Augustine had attributed to the young emperor all the virtues which, whether he possesses them or not, could be desirable in his state, had credited him with more power than in fact he possesses and had tactfully made no reference to the rebel Maximus, already acknowledged emperor of most of the West beyond the Alps. These themes were more or less obligatory for a speaker on such an occasion, but even to such ordinary themes Augustine had brought a force and originality of language and even a kind of sincerity which lifted them above the ordinary. His speech had been very well received by everyone, including, to all appearance, the emperor himself.

On the way back Nebridius and I were congratulating our friend on his performance and, as usual, Augustine took pleasure in the evident pleasure that we felt. Nebridius then said jokingly: 'It's a pity, Augustine, that some of the things that you said didn't happen to be true.'

I saw a shadow, as of pain, pass across Augustine's face; but it soon vanished and he was, I think, going to reply to Nebridius in the same light-hearted way. Just then, however, our progress was impeded and we had to walk for a little way in single file. We were in a very narrow street and most of it was occupied by an old beggar who was dancing, or attempting to dance, and singing at the top of his voice. He was very drunk and it was rather surprising that he retained any control at all over either his limbs or his voice. He contrived also, while waving his arms in time to the measure of his steps, still to grasp a flask of wine in one hand and even to drink from it in the pauses of his song. A few small boys were following behind, dancing in imitation, plainly enjoying themselves and showing none of the malice and cruelty which is usually shown by children when they see a drunken adult making a fool of himself. Possibly this was due to the fact that the old beggar, drunk and disorderly as indeed he was, somehow conveyed by his expression and even by the uncertain movements of his arms and legs a sense of complete and unreflecting happiness and confidence. A sensible man would, no doubt, be ashamed of himself, if he ever came to make such an exhibition of himself, yet the old beggar's joy, temporary as it was and artificially induced, seemed so profound and, in a sense, so selfless, that it was impossible not to feel sympathy with it. As we went past, Nebridius put a coin into the old man's hand, but he, though he mechanically called out a blessing to Nebridius, was too happy now to think of to-morrow when, in all probability, he would wake up with a sick headache and lack enough money to buy more wine for himself. Now he was wholly content and had no anticipation that his content could ever come to an end. Instead of keeping Nebridius' coin, he turned round and gave it to one of the boys who were following behind.

When we had got past the old man and were once again walking together side by side, I noticed that the expression on Augustine's face had changed to one of extreme seriousness. He did not say another word until we had turned into another street. Then he stood still and began to speak to us with such urgency that several passers-by stopped to listen, thinking perhaps that they were about to witness a quarrel or to hear some surprising news. Finding that all that he was speaking about was happiness, they soon went on their ways. Augustine had not even noticed that they had been paying him a momentary attention. 'What have we been doing all our lives,' he asked us, 'and what are we doing now except to search for happiness? All our long hours of study, all our careful plans have this final aim. We look for wisdom because we believe that wisdom will make us happy. We work at our professions so that we may be rich or famous and we think that riches and fame also can make us happy. But what happens? We tire out our eyes and our minds in our studies and are no nearer the happiness of wisdom than we were when we were children. All we have acquired is a certain dexterity in the manipulation of logical argument, and none of the arguments which we build up or pull down leads us anywhere except to discontent and a terrifying emptiness. And what is our work and our ambition? You, Alypius, are probably the least miserable of us. You are too good to be stirred beyond a certain point by the thought of honour or riches, and in dealing with justice and injustice you are at least doing something valuable. Yet even with the best intentions you know that you must often adapt your work to the hypocrisies and greed of a legal system that is neither fine nor noble, being more concerned with the acquisition or preservation of power and property than with anything else. And why did you come to Rome, Nebridius? You have told me it was because you were unhappy, you who have everything that is assumed to make for happiness. You are rich, handsome, intelligent; you have a fine property and by your own efforts you have made it still more valuable than it was. But all your work only brought you in more money that you did not want; more corn and olives and meat and wine that you could not eat or drink. And as for wisdom, your intelligence and your erudition have brought you no nearer it than Alypius and I are. Even so you are better than I am. I still feel ambition; I still love praise, like a schoolboy who is uncertain of himself. And while the work that you and Alypius do is at least sometimes admirable, there is nothing sincere or true about my profession at all. You do at least help to produce the food which keeps people alive; Alypius does at least contribute to a form of justice which is better than no justice at all. But all I do is to sell a kind of verbal trickery, and to advertise myself by elegant falsehoods, as I was doing this morning.'

Both Nebridius and I felt that he was expressing not only his own thoughts but ours as well. Yet his distress was painful to contemplate and no doubt it was in an effort to relieve it that Nebridius, speaking in a lighter tone, asked him, 'Would you rather be like that beggar whom we saw just now? He had not a care in the world. But would we all prefer to be drunkards?'

'It was just of him that I was thinking,' Augustine said. 'And though I knew I would rather be myself than he, I can really see no good reason why I should think so. His simple pleasure gives him happiness while all my carefully thought-out and strenuous interests and diversions give me nothing but pain. It is demeaning, maybe, to be drunk; but by the morning he will have slept off his drunkenness, whereas no sleep ends my anxiety. I shall be as half-hearted and as vexed a creature tomorrow as I am today. You may say that he is a slave to drink, but he is not such a slave as I am. All he needs is his bottle and that makes him happy. But I need a thousand things and none of them gives me happiness. He drinks five or six cups of wine and is content, but I, when I have laid my hands on what I desire, am no more satisfied than I was before. With a drunkard there is such a thing as satiety—such

206

a thing as rest; but when does my lust let me rest, when have I ever had all the praise that I could want? Yet I pretend to be seeking wisdom and even tell myself sometimes that I am drawing nearer to God and all the time I know that with more than half my being I am pushing God away from me and am perhaps employing my little learning in a kind of self-mystification and a hypocritical justification for my unreal vanity and my habitual lust. Much more than that harmless beggar it is I who am the drunkard and the slave.'

There was sadness as well as bitterness in his words and both Nebridius and I were anxious rather to relieve his sadness than to attempt any reasoned argument. For, though it might seem easy to demonstrate that his words were exaggerated, we realized that much of what he said was applicable to us also. He merely felt more keenly than we the dissatisfaction which was known to us all, and in face of the depth of his feeling the questions as to whether, or in what sense, the beggar was or was not better and happier than he seemed idle and meaningless exercises in debate. The real question which he was raising was, to us as to him, unanswerable. So we walked on in silence, having nothing to say which seemed worth saying and in the end it was Augustine himself who, observing our dejection, began to speak on some different topic.

This incident (and there have been others like it) served to show me what I should have known before—that no change of environment can effect any great alteration in the mind, or, if it does so, it does so gradually and insensibly. Among all the excitement, the vitality and the promise of Milan we are the same people as we were in Rome and Carthage. And I myself, I think, might go on like this for ever. I should never be quite happy, but so long as I had my friends with me, I should often be happy enough and, though I should remain conscious of my lack of understanding, I might in the end, like so many others, become used to this state. Thus I should more closely resemble the drunken beggar than Augustine and, though I might be happier than my friend, I should be much less admirable.

II

Romanianus arrived two days ago and we have already had several long talks with him. He brought with him his son, Licentius, who was a pupil of Augustine in Carthage and is now to be enrolled in his classes in Milan. Augustine is delighted to have this young man with him again, partly because he is genuinely fond of him and has a high opinion of his abilities, partly because he can now do something to make up for what he considers to have been his lack of consideration to Romanianus in leaving Africa so suddenly and so secretly. Licentius is certainly a boy of great charm and considerable intelligence. He is devoted to Augustine and Augustine responds, as always, warmly and wholeheartedly to his affection. Indeed I think, in his desire to see nothing but good in his friends, he gives the young man credit for more talent and a steadier character than he actually possesses. For while Licentius is wildly and charmingly excited about what immediately attracts him in his studies, he is reluctant to make the least effort to do anything that he does not like doing. Here he is very unlike Augustine's own son, Adeodatus, who is not only extremely intelligent, but thorough, and whose nature is uniformly sweet and gentle, showing none of those alternations between high spirits and sulkiness that I notice in Licentius. Augustine himself of course notices the young man's faults and is distressed by them. But Licentius has only to laugh at himself and to promise to do better and

Augustine will be delighted at the openness of his nature and believes that the momentary sincerity of his words is likely to be lasting. This is characteristic of him. Certainly I know that in his affection he has always had far too high an opinion of me also.

Nebridius, of course, had seen Romanianus fairly recently, but I had not seen him for years, and Augustine not for a considerable time. He is much older than I am; indeed he must be nearly fifty. As he is a kinsman and friend of my father, I was brought up to look up to him. It was only after he came to know and to love Augustine that he began to treat me as a friend, rather than as a mere boy. Thus I began to see him not only as a distinguished and impressive figure but as a warm-hearted man, open and generous and bursting with enthusiasm. In public, whether by training or by nature, he always carries himself with great dignity. Even in Milan he stands out from the crowd as one entitled to respect. His great height, firm features, and strangely melancholy eyes attract attention wherever he is. As a rule, too, he will dress magnificently, though in excellent taste. His fair hair curls naturally and on him one or two jewels appear with greater splendour and distinction than do the heavy weights of gold and precious stones that are carried by many of the rich and powerful. He conceives it to be his duty, I think, to show himself to advantage, for he is devoted to our town and to the whole district and, as the most important man there, wants to do his own part to make others see that their portion of Africa is not without distinction.

But when he is alone with his friends he will relax entirely. The severity and apparent indifference of his expression change to a look of warmth, gaiety and an eager inquisitiveness. He shows interest in every detail, however trivial, in his friends' lives, will praise them extravagantly for any success which they may have had and will make every kind of excuse for their failures, however deserved. In this extreme generosity of affection he resembles Augustine.

So at our first meeting with Romanianus much of the time was taken up in answering his inquiries as to what we had been doing and in listening to his congratulations which were given to each of us in turn, though in fact neither Nebridius nor I had done anything noteworthy at all since we had been in Milan. But to Romanianus our studies in Neo-Platonism and our new interest in Ambrose's explanation of the Christian faith were in themselves objects of admiration and themes for enthusiasm.

All this time I could see, however, that he had something else on his mind and our accounts of our studies served as an introduction to it. He had already, of course, discussed with Nebridius his plan of forming a community which was to be devoted to philosophy and the search for the good life. Now he addressed himself in particular to Augustine and myself. We were sitting in the garden of the house that he had rented in Milan, very much at our ease now, for the excitement of our first meeting was wearing off and, after his eager greetings and interrogations, we were feeling relaxed and happy in the first cool breeze of evening. It was evident that Romanianus had something to say and that he wanted to say it at once. But for a moment or two he seemed to be rigorously restraining himself, as though he was aiming at imparting, by suspense, additional weight to the words he was about to speak. First he called a servant and ordered some wine, and then, when he had filled our cups, he took from his neck the gold chain which he was wearing and laid it on the table by his side. The gestures appeared involuntary and yet it gave the impression that he was deliberately divesting himself of the outward marks of rank and wealth, and I found it strangely moving. He began to speak slowly but as he went on his words came faster and faster, indicating an enthusiasm and excitement which, with the best will in the world, he could not control.

'My friends,' he said, 'Nebridius will have told you already of our discussions in Africa. But think back now to the time when I first began to know you. Up to then I had spent my adult life in doing what I considered to be my duty in the affairs of our town and the province. I took pleasure in holding various magistracies, in presiding over the games, in the organization of new buildings and gardens. My social life was rich and varied. I took care, to the best of my ability, of my family and my estate. Most people regarded me as being peculiarly fortunate and that, I suppose, was the opinion which I held of myself, too. It was only after I came to know you three young men that my views both of myself and of my surroundings changed. Oh, yes, you have made me discontented and there are times when my wife is inclined to blame you for that. But you need not blame yourselves. I am happier in my discontent than I was when I falsely believed myself to be happy.'

Here he paused for a moment and smiled at us. There was a warmth and a geniality in his smile. It did indeed seem that he was happy, and I could not help contrasting his attitude with that of Augustine on those occasions when he was lamenting his incapacity to see the truth or both to know and to do what was right. Romanianus, on the other hand, seemed to be, if not content with his inadequacy, at least glad to know that it existed and confident that somehow it could be overcome. Augustine's agony of mind proceeded not only from his inability to find the truth, but also from a deep dissatisfaction with himself. Indeed he would often attribute his intellectual blindness to what he conceived to be his own moral delinquency. No such pangs afflicted Romanianus. In his own character and actions he had nothing to hide, nothing of which to be ashamed; and, knowing that he was sincere in his search for truth, he attributed his ignorance simply to lack of instruction or to intellectual errors which, with proper care and attention, could certainly be remedied. Undoubtedly most people would regard him as a more balanced and integrated character than Augustine. His generosity, his confidence and his warmth gave strength and courage to us all. I myself loved him for these qualities; and yet I seemed to recognize in my affection some elements of those feelings which we entertain for some noble animal, a horse or a dog, creatures of real excellence which we love and yet at the same time almost pity, since in their innocence they are unable to share in our own sorrows. I myself cannot fully share in the feelings of Augustine when he is most miserable, yet I can sympathize with him and can recognize that his agony is real, since I have experienced something of the same kind myself. He is conscious of evil and of degeneration, and, as it seems to me, these things exist. Romanianus, it may be said, is mercifully debarred from perceiving them or at least from taking them seriously. His strength and his native optimism have convinced him that for every ill there is a remedy. This may be true, but it is necessary first to recognize the extent and the violence of the ill, and this, perhaps from goodness, perhaps from stupidity, he does not do.

He went on speaking, addressing himself now chiefly to Augustine. 'It was you,' he said, 'Augustine, who showed me how empty of reality my life was. You did not mean to do so, and probably you have long forgotten the occasion which I have in mind. It was soon after I came to know you and I was talking to you one evening in my house of what your prospects might be when you had finished your education at Carthage. I was telling you that, with your abilities, you might become a professor of rhetoric, might even rise to some such a post as the one which you now hold and might go on to become a governor of a province, a famous poet or an official of the highest rank. I spoke of the honours you would bring to Thagaste and to Africa as a whole, and of the happiness you would find yourself in wealth, power and reputation. You were a very young man then and your eyes lit up with pleasure while I was speaking. You began to thank me for what you imagined to be my generosity, though it was no generosity at all, for if I was able to be of some help to you at that time, it was at no sacrifice to myself, and indeed I was looking at the prospect of your future success simply as another plan for bringing distinction to our town and, in a sense, to myself. I think it was to please me that you showed such delight in what I was saying, for I know how diffident you are with regard to your abilities, and probably you did not believe that you could ever reach the high positions which I was speaking of, though, as we see, I happened to be right. And then (I shall never forget it) your face took on an expression of even more radiant delight and anticipation. "And I might become wise too," you said, "and that would be better than all the rest." I was charmed by your enthusiasm, but quite astounded by your simple words. For how, I wondered, could this prospect excite you, as it evidently did, so much more than the thought of what nearly all men most desire—wealth, honour and power? You went on to speak to me of a book you had been reading. It was, I think, the *Hortensius* of Cicero. And you spoke with a kind of rapture, as though you were possessed by some God. I listened quietly and in a kind of amazement. You know how difficult it is for me to be quiet, but then it seemed to me that I was hearing the words not of a boy who, however talented, was a creature like myself, but of a higher power. You noticed nothing of this and before long began to excuse yourself for talking too long and too egotistically. But I could have listened for ever, and there was nothing egotistic about your words. In fact your self had disappeared in what I can only call a radiance of glory.'

While Romanianus was speaking, I glanced from time to time at Augustine and could see that he was struggling with a variety of emotions. His face expressed sadness, impatience, embarrassment and even a kind of anger. I knew that the anger was directed at himself and that the sadness was something like despair as he contemplated the eager fervour and confidence of his early youth and compared it to his present state, a state which to Romanianus and indeed to many others appeared fortunate but in which he himself was so far from satisfied. I thought that he would burst out into bitter invective against himself, utterly disclaiming all the merits which Romanianus saw in him and I trembled for the peace of mind of Romanianus himself in his happy mood of confidence and affection. Probably Nebridius shared my fear, for he broke in quickly. 'And I know,' he said, 'what our friend Romanianus is going to say next. He is going to tell us that he has discovered a method by which we can all become wise overnight.'

The short interruption was enough to enable Augustine to regain control of himself. The lines of his face softened as he smiled. 'Go on, Romanianus,' he said, 'and tell us all about it. But don't say any more about me. You make me sad, because I am not and never was as good as you think.'

He was trying to speak lightly and yet there was a force and urgency in the tone of his voice which seemed to unsettle Romanianus. He opened his mouth as though to protest, but then thought better of it. 'Very well,' he said, laughing. 'I'll do as you say, even though everything I've said is true and you are far too modest. But let me say first that ever since that time I too have been in my own limited way a lover of wisdom and have come to see, first dimly and then more and more clearly, that there is nothing in life of equal importance. I began, as you know, by trying to make up some of the gaps in my education. I read books that I had never read before or had read with insufficient attention and I soon felt that I was making at least some progress. Then Alypius and Augustine went to Italy and I seemed to see less and less of Nebridius. Other friends with whom I talked lacked either the knowledge or the enthusiasm which you three have and somehow I found myself becoming more heavy-witted and less hopeful than I had been. Suddenly it dawned on me that almost every important operation of life has to be carried out with the aid of others. A man cannot build a great building with his own two hands, nor can one man fight a battle. I saw that it was with the help of my friends that I had been making what progress I had made towards wisdom and I like to think that there were times, too, when I myself have contributed something of value to our discussions. But you, for one reason or another, were now living far from me. I felt myself declining from the point to which I had advanced and I wondered whether you too might perhaps be in something of the same predicament. It seemed a cruel necessity. But then, in a flash, I realized that this was not a necessity at all. For there is nothing whatever to prevent us from living together and devoting our whole lives to the pursuit which we value most. I have enough money for all of us. Everything suddenly seemed simple. As you know, I immediately discussed my plan with Nebridius, and he insisted that, if it were adopted, he also would wish to contribute to its cost. But all that is of secondary importance. We might, for example, all pool our resources and adopt whatever system seemed to us most appropriate for administering our common property. Each individual in our community might have his task to do in sharing out the burden of practical affairs. Or we might, as in the old republic, appoint two magistrates each year and vest all authority in them. There are a hundred different methods by which we might arrive at the desired result— a life free from material anxiety, self-chosen, based on friendship and the co-operative search for wisdom. Now what do you think of this idea?'

But he was himself too eagerly enthusiastic for his plan to allow us time to answer his question. As though taking our approval for granted he went straight on speaking. 'The first question to be decided,' he said, 'would be the precise constitution of our little group. There would be, of course, the four of us here and there are other friends of ours in Africa whom we might consider inviting to join. Personally I should like my son Licentius to be one of our number and no doubt Augustine would like Adeodatus to join us too. But of course in all this question of membership it would be necessary for the whole community to be agreed. All I will say now is that we all know how brilliant a boy Adeodatus is and, as for

Licentius, Augustine has often told me that he too, though inclined to be lazy, has real ability and a true desire to improve himself.'

While he had been speaking Licentius had quietly joined us and had been listening to his father's words. He now spoke impulsively and with an enthusiasm so like that of Romanianus himself that we were all both amused and charmed. 'Do let me join,' he said. 'It would mean more to me than anything. I know I'm often bad-tempered and lazy, but I could get better. I know I could, easily.'

He spoke with real urgency and his eyes were full of tears. At the same time the beginnings of a smile seemed to be trembling on his lips. It was as though he knew (though he was, I am sure, unconscious of the knowledge) that he was too attractive to be refused anything. And of course we all agreed that he must certainly become one of us.

So, insensibly, we began to discuss the membership of our community before we had reached any very precise definition of its aims or possibilities. And as we went on speaking it began to occur to me that, though in a general sense we were all united in our desire to attain wisdom, this was a term which, however glorious, was capable of many different interpretations. It seemed to me too that if we were ever to understand the full meaning of such words as 'truth' or 'happiness' we should first have to discover or to stumble upon the right approach and it was beginning to look as though this path, if it existed, was more likely to be stumbled upon than to be discovered by any rational process. Romanianus, in his more confident moments, might compare his project with that of the Academy of Plato or of the Garden of Epicurus. But there was an important difference. Both Plato and Epicurus had believed themselves to be on the right path. We had no such assurance and, though able to understand and even to admire philosophers of the past, had discovered none with much relevance to the present and the future.

These misgivings of mine must have occurred also to

Augustine and Nebridius, but all of us, I think, were so carried away by the infectious enthusiasm of Romanianus that we scarcely allowed them at the time a lodging in our minds. Instead we discussed the project gaily and eagerly, as though it were already a reality and successful.

Nebridius was first to suggest that our friend Ventidius would be an invaluable addition to our group. I myself have only recently come to know this most agreeable and intelligent man who is already a friend of both Nebridius and Augustine. He is one of the best professors of grammar in Milan and was eager to make the acquaintance of Augustine as soon as he arrived. They soon found that they had more in common than their interest in literature, for it seems that for the last ten years Ventidius has been following just the same lines of inquiry and has been beset by just the same difficulties and doubts as we have in our search for truth. At first it seemed to us remarkable and surprising that, without any contact between us, Ventidius in Milan and we in Africa or Rome should have been thinking so alike and should have known the same urgency and the same disappointments. Soon, however, we saw that there is nothing remarkable about this. Probably all over the world there are thousands and tens of thousands with the same perplexities all suffering from the same tremulation between hope and despair. What was really remarkable was that we should have imagined ourselves to be unique. And indeed there is some comfort in the realization that we are not alone. Ventidius has not only given us this comfort but made us feel ashamed of ourselves for having regarded ourselves as isolated when in fact we were not.

It now seemed to us only right and natural that he should be invited to join our group and we are making arrangements to consult him about it tomorrow. Personally I can foresee some difficulty here, for Ventidius is devoted to his school and, though he could well afford it, he would be very reluctant not to fulfil all his obligations to his pupils. Nebridius is implicated here too, since for the last few weeks he has been helping Ventidius in his work. He came to do this almost, as it were, accidentally, but in a way that shows his generosity and also the extreme conscientiousness of Ventidius. For Nebridius had been urging him to hire an assistant teacher, since he seemed to be working too hard for the good of his health, and Ventidius was explaining that the kind of teacher whom he would accept was unobtainable. Anyone who was up to what he regarded as the required standard would start a school of his own rather than take a subordinate post and he was not prepared to subject his students to the kind of second-rate instruction which seemed to be all that was available. 'I should be delighted,' he said, 'if I could find someone with half your knowledge of literature, but I can't.' Nebridius had immediately, and greatly to the surprise of Ventidius, offered to help him. He appears to enjoy the work almost as much as he enjoys being able to render a valuable service to his friend. Of course he is not bound by any obligation to continue in it and now, as we talked in the garden with Romanianus, we all seemed somehow to assume that all of us, including Ventidius, would be not only glad but able to join in the community which we were planning. But in fact I shall be very surprised if, when we see him tomorrow, he shows himself willing to give up work which, however arduous, he regards as valuable and, as I reflect on his probable attitude, I find myself admiring it, for there seems to be something lacking in our plans. For though they have a worthy basis in our sincere friendship and our shared desires for wisdom and for right living, they may also imply a rigid separation of ourselves from the rest of the world and from some ordinary and honourable obligations.

III

How strange it is that in those whom we know most intimately so much may often lie concealed from us! That those who are most frank and open with us may on certain occasions preserve a silence that we should never have expected and indeed, knowing their characters, could never expect! It is this thought that I find most startling, for in the actual events which have occurred there was nothing which I could not have anticipated. But why was it that Augustine at no time gave me so much as a hint of what was going on? Not that I blame him for this. I am not one of those who consider that their friends have betrayed them unless they are allowed to share their every thought, and in this case I can see that Augustine may well have decided that it would be unfair to me to implicate me in a situation where my advice and feelings could not have carried much weight.

But how is it that I myself could have been so insensitive and so blind? I had even imagined that in Augustine's household things were going better than I had hoped or expected. It is true that I have often noticed on Lucilla's face an expression of sadness, but it was a sadness of resignation with no anger or bitterness about it such as I have seen in Rome. I noticed too that Augustine was being more than usually tender with her and that Monnica also has been treating her with great kindness and even with a kind of deference. They have been constantly going to church together and in their conversation have been speaking as though there was some kind of a secret understanding between them. I had assumed this understanding to have been of a religious character—and indeed perhaps it is. Both of them are devoted to the preaching of Bishop Ambrose and much of their talk has been based on his sermons. In these talks Augustine too has often joined. He is never arrogant in conversation, but it is natural with him to be incisive in expressing his views. Now, however, when speaking of religious subjects he is showing a new kind of diffidence and I have imagined that both the two women have been pleased to find him listening so respectfully to their words and, perhaps more important, to see that he is drawing nearer and nearer to the point where he may wish to be baptized. This also, no doubt, is true and, now that I come to think of it, he will be better able to seek baptism after the change which has been decided upon and which Lucilla seems to have accepted without complaint, although I still find it difficult to believe that either he or she can regard it without pain.

Nor do I think that Augustine himself is really acting with that sincerity of purpose which he would like to have and which he believes that he does have. This is a hard thing to say of him, since he, more than anyone I have known, is quick to perceive and to understand what is true and what is false in the often obscure motivations of conduct. In this case, however, he seems to me to be forcing himself to adopt a conviction and a state of mind which is not precisely his own, though of course he insists that it is. Or (since such behaviour is so unlike him) it may perhaps be said that this conviction and this state of mind are in a very profound way his own, but that in the present instance he has not reached them perfectly and completely. It is as though he had come to a right conclusion in a mathematical problem by means of a faulty process of reasoning. In particular I mistrust his apparent calm. This again is unlike him. Always before when he has reached a position in thought or action where he could feel perfectly confident, he has not only been full of joy and excitement himself, but would communicate these feelings to all about him.

So yesterday it was his manner almost as much as what he said which startled and perplexed me. He had called for me so that we might walk together to the house of Ventidius, where Romanianus, Nebridius and one or two others were to join us. He found me reading one of the Letters of the Apostle Paul. Ambrose had recently been preaching on this Letter and I wished to verify one of the references he had made to it. I happened to mention to Augustine that Paul's views on marriage and on virginity seemed very like those held by the monk Jerome, whom I had met on the Aventine Hill. Augustine agreed with me, though he pointed out that people were apt to exaggerate these views. 'For instance,' he said, 'it would be wrong to suggest that Paul ever condemned marriage.'

I fancied that he was thinking of some discussions which we had had already about whether or not woman could play a useful part in a philosophical community such as the one which we were planning. On this point both Nebridius and I were somewhat uncertain, while Augustine and Romanianus would argue with great fervour that the companionship of women, so far from being a handicap to our researches was, to them at least, something indispensable. They had given us the names of many good and wise men who had been married. Paul, of course, was not, but it was perfectly true that many of his trusted friends and helpers in the early Church had been married women. I was expecting Augustine to develop this theme, but instead he turned away from me and said, in a strangely earnest tone of voice, 'By the way, Alypius, I am going to get married myself.'

Somehow this bold statement seemed to me incredible, although I had often in fact speculated on the possibility that he might at some time, for one reason or another, decide to take this step. Monnica, I knew, had often pressed him to do so, partly, I believe, from motives of jealousy of which, to do her justice, she was probably unaware, and partly, no doubt, because she sincerely wished him to conform to the rules of the Christian religion, so that he would be in a fit state to receive baptism. Recently, however, her attitude towards

Lucilla and Lucilla's towards her seemed to have changed from one of scarcely veiled animosity to one of genuine friendship. Now I suddenly began to see the reason for this change and it appeared to me (though I do not quite know why) appalling. It was not that I could not see that there might be good reasons for the decision that had evidently been made. It might even be that the decision was the right one. But what I found unbearable to contemplate was the certain misery of Lucilla and of Augustine himself; and that they would be miserable seemed to me beyond doubt; for I did not believe in the reality or in the durability of the attitudes which they were now adopting. I uttered the one word 'Lucilla', and in speaking I must by my expression or by the tone of my voice have indicated to him that I had received his information not only with surprise but with a kind of horror.

He laid his hand upon my arm and spoke to me gently, as though he were attempting to console me on some sorrow of my own; and again his manner appeared strange to me; for what distressed me was not my own pain but the thought of his. 'Dear Alypius,' he said, 'you are right to think of her and you will know how much I too have thought of her. She is good. She is so much better than I am.'

These last words were spoken with the kind of feeling I am used to expecting in him. Then he seemed to check himself, changed his tone of voice and began again to speak calmly and precisely as though he were expounding to me some difficult, but necessary, proposition. 'What is important,' he said, 'is that we are doing what is right and that we both know it. It is natural that we should feel pain at first but, as my mother says, to do right cannot lead to pain in the end. It must lead to joy. My mother has been wonderfully good throughout all this. She has been so kind and considerate to Lucilla and you must have noticed how Lucilla loves her.'

As he seemed to be waiting for a reply, I said that I had

indeed noticed this. My reply appeared to satisfy him and he went on speaking with greater ease. I thought both his ease and his fluency strangely unnatural.

'Lucilla is giving up much more than I am,' he said. 'She is leaving Adeodatus with me, not only for his sake (since I can give him a better education), but also for mine. She knows how much I love him, but she loves him too and it is a terrible sacrifice for a mother to give up her son.'

'Is she going back to Africa?' I asked; and it seemed to me that I was speaking as unnaturally as he was.

'Yes,' he said, 'at the end of this month. And here too she is showing herself better and stronger than I am. She has vowed never to sleep with another man after she has left me. She will altogether withdraw from the life of the world and is going to enter a religious house.'

I thought of the time in Rome when Lucilla had told me that this, or something like it, was her intention if ever she became parted from Augustine. Then she had been deeply and terribly distressed and had made it clear, even perhaps with a kind of cynicism, that this was the last thing which she wanted to happen. 'How,' she had said, 'could this be God's will?' Since then she had had time to consider things further and perhaps she had at last come to the conclusion that this was indeed the will of God. If so her resignation was possibly understandable. But the calm with which Augustine was speaking was not to me understandable at all. Until recently he cannot even have contemplated this separation. I listened to him as he went on speaking.

'It was my mother,' he said, 'who persuaded first Lucilla and then me that this is what we ought to do. She made all the arrangements, though she did not start to do so until she knew that both Lucilla and I were beginning to see that her plans were the best ones that could be made for us. She pointed out what is quite true, that I'm bound to be somewhat handicapped in my career unless I am able to ally myself with some powerful and influential family here. Not that

I, as you know, am much concerned about this; but Lucilla regards this as important and so does my mother.'

He was still speaking with a quite extraordinary ease, even with a kind of lightness. In fact I was scarcely able to believe that this was indeed my friend speaking. Not that he is without ambition. I know that thoughts of power and honour have often appealed to him. But always and invariably he relegates these to a secondary place among his real desires. Indeed he is often ashamed of harbouring such thoughts at all. I could see certainly that these considerations would have weight with Lucilla. She has long regarded herself as an impediment to him and in her love for him there is a considerable element of gratitude. But Augustine himself has never thought in this way, and so I was astonished to find him speaking now as his mother might speak or as Lucilla might be encouraged to speak. No doubt my surprise was evident, for he went on quickly and was now beginning to appear rather as though he were defending himself than as one who was simply stating facts.

'You are thinking,' he said, 'that it is unlike me to be talking like this of honours and wealth and influential connections. And it would be, if this were all that was in my mind. But there is much else besides. What influences me most is the thought that neither my life nor Lucilla's is as good as it might be. Even if I felt fit to be baptized, I should rightly be refused baptism. For it is not and it cannot be Christian married love that brings Lucilla and me together. From the beginning we had no thought of such a relationship. We sought nothing but the gratification of our desires.'

I have often heard him speak like this before and cannot fully understand the argument. So now I said nothing, though he gave me a questioning look, as though seeking my assent.

'Not everyone,' he went on, 'can be naturally pure and good as you are. And on this my mother is very understanding. She admits that in most cases it is natural, especially for men and especially in our youth, to be carried away by these uncontrollable passions. But these passions in themselves can never be good and must often be cruel, inconsiderate and perverse. Yet God had made it possible for them to be controlled and even, in a way, sanctified. Marriage, consecrated by the Church and entered into deliberately with the purpose of raising children, is an utterly different thing from a union which has come into existence and subsists only, or even mainly, on a mutuality of physical desire. Chastity is no doubt a holier thing still; but I am not fit for that, or not yet.'

Again he was speaking in a way that was not quite like himself. Not that he was saying what he did not believe. I knew that for a long time, even in the days when he was a Manichaean, his thoughts had been turning in this direction, and that recently, under the influence of Bishop Ambrose and of his mother, this way of thought had found a firmer intellectual basis and so had become for him still more compelling. Yet it had seemed to me that the more he became convinced of the desirability of chastity, the more he had suffered. He had been fully aware that, while he desired chastity, he did not want to be chaste. His pleasure with Lucilla was, as he has often said, as much a part of himself as an arm or a leg. Moreover for some sixteen or seventeen years his love had been confined to her. Yet now, from the way he was talking, it seemed to me that she was becoming to him a mere abstraction. Since he was proposing to get married, he was evidently not going to give up the pleasures of sex. And I had no doubt that whoever it was whom he was going to marry could not possibly be so important to him as Lucilla was. I knew indeed that, however he might speak, Lucilla was in fact no abstraction to him. How then could he adopt this doctrinaire manner, this apparent ease and confidence? It almost seemed that by explaining and approving the Christian view of marriage, he had already convinced himself that he had accepted it. These thoughts confused and troubled me. Even now I can scarcely put them into words, so puzzling do I find them. For usually when people behave unnaturally, it is a mark of insincerity; but Augustine cannot be insincere and I do not like to think of him as being blind. At the time all I could do was to inquire the name of the lady whom he proposed to marry.

He named the daughter of an official at the court, a man of great wealth and considerable influence. He is a Christian himself and his wife, who is known for her exceptional piety, has, probably for this reason, become closely acquainted with Monnica who helps her in the organization of various charities for the poor, the sick and the bereaved. It is a powerful and respected family and it occurred to me that Monnica herself could have desired no better alliance for her son. I have some slight acquaintance with them, but, so far as I could remember, they had only one daughter, a very beautiful child who cannot be more than twelve years old. It appeared that my recollection was correct.

'You have met her and her family,' Augustine was saying, 'and of course I cannot marry her for two years. She is too young.'

Since this was so, I wondered why it was necessary for Lucilla to leave so soon. As Augustine explained this to me he began at last to speak as I might have expected him to speak, revealing that he was in reality much more distressed by her approaching departure than he had seemed to be and perhaps more than he imagined himself to be.

'Everything,' he said, 'has been arranged by my mother; and when I say this, you may perhaps think that she has in some way forced us into this situation. This is completely untrue. She has consulted Lucilla at every step and I am sure that she would never have proceeded with her plans unless she had got her approval first.'

I could not help wondering whether this last statement was indeed true. I could see however that without the co-operation of Lucilla, Monnica would have found it extremely difficult to induce Augustine to make this alliance, advantageous as it was.

'I am not worthy,' he was saying, 'of either of those two women. Of course I have long known this so far as my mother is concerned. She has always had a truer faith and a clearer insight into things than I have. Recently, indeed, I have seen that my way of life is wrong, that I could never receive baptism while living in sin, that I should curb my pleasures and submit to the rule of marriage. But I could never have done this by myself. And I had thought that Lucilla would be the last person to give me just the help I needed. But now she has shown herself stronger and much better than I can be. No doubt she has been helped in this by my mother, but I too have had the same help and am still not capable of the same resolution. I can see more clearly than she can the uncleanliness of our love. It is too violent; its satisfaction is in itself and therefore must distract us from God. Yet, though I see all this and she, I think, hardly sees it at all, I could never have given up this love unless she herself had urged me to do so. Also, while I am leaving her to get married, she is leaving me for a better state than that. For though marriage is not a sin, there can be sin in marriage. But Lucilla, when she leaves me and goes back to Africa, will take vows of chastity and will be for ever beyond the reach of that sin and that distress. And I, in my selfishness, would actually have impeded her in this resolution. If it had been possible, I would have wished to keep her with me until the time of my wedding drew near, and because of my selfish demands, she would have been willing to stay. It was my mother who pointed out that this would be quite impossible. If one has once decided that one's way of life is wrong, or could be improved, it is clearly one's duty to change it at once. But, though this point is perfectly obvious, I know well that one does not always do what is right, and I think that Lucilla and I would have gone on living in the same way if it had not been that the family of my future wife had insisted that there could be no engagement so long as I was living with another woman. This is natural, of course—especially with parents who are fond of their daughter and are devout Christians themselves. And my mother has shown us that it is not only natural, but good for us both.'

His words failed entirely to relieve my anxiety and my disquiet; and yet now, when I look on them, I wonder how far I was justified in feeling as I did. Somehow the words seemed to me surprising and unconvincing, and yet they were logical enough; they expressed nothing that I had not heard expressed before with sincerity and sense by Ambrose, by many Christians and indeed by Augustine himself. And if I were to say that it was his manner, his calm, that struck me as strange and unnatural, might not this mean simply that I am still incapable of understanding a nature so much richer and stronger than my own? Am I, perhaps, so sentimentally embedded in a past which was once real that I resent the idea of any change, any development? For certainly I did feel a kind of resentment, and, since I am incapable of resenting anything in Augustine himself, I began in my thoughts to blame (but for what?) his mother Monnica. Suppose her to have been, as indeed she has been in the past, jealous of Lucilla, it still does not follow that her actions with regard to this marriage were either wrong or insincere; nor does it mean that the affection which now she seems to feel for Lucilla is not genuine. No doubt she can now see in Lucilla qualities of whose existence she was unaware—a willingness to sacrifice herself for what she believes to be the best interests of the man she loves, a new kind of piety, a wholehearted desire to follow the way which Ambrose and others have declared to be the way of God. And Lucilla on her side may see in Monnica no longer the jealousy and possessiveness of a mother, but that same profound and unselfish desire for Augustine's good which she feels herself.

All this may be true, and if so, why am I still uneasy? People, and perhaps particularly women, can take a positive delight in making sacrifices which, however painful, seem to them necessary or desirable, and it may be that in a certain sense Lucilla will grow to feel a satisfaction and a security greater than that which she now has. Certainly she is taking one of those definite and irrevocable steps in life which, if taken whole-heartedly and for the right reasons, seem to secure for people a lasting and a growing satisfaction. And certainly she appears to be whole-hearted.

Perhaps what worries me is that Augustine, whatever he may think, is not taking a step comparable with hers. That her departure will cause him acute pain I have no doubt and he will miss her for herself and not only because of the pleasures that they share together. Yet while he, too, is making a sacrifice for what he believes to be right, it is not, as with her, one of a permanent and conclusive nature. In two years' time he will be enjoying the embraces of another woman and though for one of his habits two years is a long time, it is not for ever. I have no doubt that Jerome would say that of the two of them Lucilla is the happiest and he may be right. And others, no doubt (Praetextatus, for instance), would say that neither of them is happy, that they are both unhappy victims of an unnatural ideal, throwing away a state of life which is normal and in a true sense blessed by the Gods for the sake of an abstention (incomplete and hypocritical in the case of Augustine) which is commended not by God or nature, but only by theorists, monks and bishops.

Certainly my uneasiness at the news I had heard prevented me from taking much part in the discussions at the house of Ventidius. Augustine, however, talked more than usual and it still seemed to me that he was talking unnaturally. There was something almost feverish in the vigour with which he supported Romanianus in the view that the married state is desirable, if not necessary, for a philosopher. Others disagreed and others, while agreeing, owned that their wives were wholly averse from any such society as that which we were planning. I should not be surprised if the whole scheme were to break down on this point.

IV

Now that I take up my diary again I see that the last words I wrote in it were prophetic. Also I fear that the anxiety I was feeling then about Augustine was fully justified, though here matters are more obscure, and painful too for me to contemplate.

As for the cummunity planned with such confidence and enthusiasm by Romanianus, not many more discussions were required to make it clear that the idea would have to be abandoned. In the first place Ventidius, as I had expected, reluctantly but firmly refused to join. His duty, he said, was to his pupils; the work was necessary to him and he enjoyed it. Romanianus attempted to make him change his mind, telling him that if he was deterred by any financial considerations—the need, for instance, to support a mother or sisters—he would himself gladly take the responsibility of meeting any or all of these obligations. Ventidius appeared embarrassed by this generosity and to us, too, it seemed that Romanianus, with the best and kindest of intentions, was guilty of a certain lack of delicacy. His mind was so set on his plan that he was unable to imagine that any intelligent person could think of it differently from himself. And therefore he was concluding that there was no impediment which could not be removed by a sufficient quantity of money. In fact Ventidius is quite well off. He runs his school not in order to make money but because he enjoys the work and considers that in doing it he is performing a valuable social service, as indeed he is. On this point Romanianus attempted to argue with him. He too, he said, had devoted much of his life to public duty; he had built baths and theatres and had done something to beautify almost every town in his neighbourhood. In none of these actions had he found any lasting satisfaction; only when, again from a sense of public duty, he had given to Augustine the help needed to continue his studies had he felt himself amply and abundantly rewarded. Was this not a proof that friendship came above social duty and that learning was worth all the monuments in the world?

Ventidius gently pointed out that in using this argument Romanianus was in fact conceding the very point which he was making. 'I too,' he said, 'derive satisfaction from attempting to improve the abilities which my pupils possess and there are some of them whom I love. Between this kind of social duty and friendship there is no necessary incompatibility.' He went on to offer us the use of his villa at Cassiciacum in the hills above Milan. This is a beautiful place to which Augustine, Nebridius and I have been several times already with Ventidius during holidays. The house itself and the gentle landscape surrounding it are ideally adapted for reading, discussions and meditation. I have walked there in the hills from sunrise to sunset, often going barefoot, since I love the feel of the earth and even, through long usage, the stones under my feet, and I have been amused to find at the end of the day Augustine admiring me for making these expeditions. He himself, though he loves every sight, sound and odour in the countryside, is more delicate than I am and cannot take much exercise. Also he is less moved than I am by those long views and changing extents of landscape which seem to travel with one when one is walking. He, on the other hand, will watch for an hour on end a lizard on the wall, taking in the colour, the texture and the movement of each limb. He is overcome with wonder at each detail of a flower or a leaf and no doubt observes more as he sits for a few hours in a garden than I have done after walking for thirty or more miles.

I myself was delighted with this offer of Ventidius. Moreover I was more than partly in agreement with him when he went on to say: 'I myself, of course, could only join you during holidays and you may not be willing to have me in your community under those conditions. But, to tell you the truth, I would in any case prefer to be a partial than a full member. Frankly I cannot approve of cutting oneself off entirely from the world in which we live. We may, and probably do, find much in our society that is disgusting. But it exists and we are part of it. Even those Christian monks (or the best of them) come back at some time or other from the desert, perhaps simply impelled by human nature, perhaps convinced that they have a duty to do something, whatever it may be, for the good of their fellow men or for the glory of God. And you will find very few philosophers who commend a total withdrawal from the world. You may say that Plato was uniquely concerned with forms that lie beyond sense. Yet till the end of his life he was attempting to incorporate the insensible in a real political and educational framework. I know too how much you all admire Bishop Ambrose. Certainly he spends some hours every day in prayer and reading, but much the greater part of his time is taken up in practical work—administration, preaching, even politics.'

Romanianus, still enthusiastic for his idea, continued for some time to dispute the validity of these views, using arguments which had often been used before by Augustine, but to Nebridius and me and several others it appeared that Ventidius was talking sense. Augustine himself was strangely undecided. Indeed he seemed to feel more strongly than any of the rest of us the attractions now of one, now of the other side of the argument. Later when I talked to him by himself he confessed that this was exactly how he did feel, and he was distressed by the very clarity of his perception. 'How can it be,' he said, 'that when I think of the delights of a life of pure contemplation and prayer, I can think of nothing sweeter? I already feel, as if this were really true, near God, filled with his love and loving all mankind and every insect and animal and leaf. I know that this is the highest and best state that there can be. And then, in a second or a fraction of a second, I see equally clearly other pleasures, worthy ones too—

scholarship, power well and wisely exercised, pious and sincere embraces, the struggle with the world as it is. In the one life there is nothing but the purest peace and beauty but in the other there is the strength of achievement and a kind of glory. One is the life of an angel or of a blessed soul, but I am not an angel and my soul is irresolute and unclean. Should I not choose the life of a man and be humble?' Here he broke off for a moment and then went on speaking in a still more agitated manner. 'But I am not humble. Sometimes I pretend to be, but I am not. I want the best, always the best. That is not wrong in itself, but what is wrong is that, whatever I may pretend, I think that I deserve the best. But how can I deserve anything? If there is any good in me, every bit of it was given me by God; and as for the evil, I chose it deliberately myself in preference to the good; I turned my back on God; I forged my own chains and now these chains of long habit tie me down, and though I feel their weight and their constriction, I would be uneasy without that familiar weight and I derive a sensual pleasure from the chafing and irritation of my bonds. I am too inured to slavery to want to be free, or to want it long enough or sincerely enough. It may be that once, long ago, God in his mercy made me fit for that peace and beauty and continual blaze of love which I can still sometimes imagine. But I chose deformity instead of beauty and now I wonder whether it would not be more honest of me to make something of what I am rather than to go on trying to be something that, owing to my own sin, I can never be. What is wrong with a normal life, if one is not good enough to be exceptional? I see now, and I see more clearly every day, that the Christian religion is true. And it is a gentle and an embracing faith. There is room in it for all men and it acknowledges our imperfections. Can I not be happy in it with marriage, with friends, with honour? Can I not be content and useful in the level world without straining for heights that are beyond my strength? Would not this be, indeed, to show at last some humility?'

He was developing ideas which had often occurred to me. For a moment I thought suddenly of Praetextatus, and I imagined Augustine living as he had lived, active and yet calm, with a different faith yet still a firm one, distinguished, honoured and content. He has the abilities for such a life and in our days one need not be a great noble in order to reach a high position. I myself, I thought, though in a humbler way, could be happy with my friends, and with a little distinction I might perhaps get married. I no longer shrink from this, although I should like any such relationship into which I enter to be stable and lasting. And then in a flash I realized that in fact I, with my shallower and less intense nature, would be much better equipped for such a life than Augustine could ever be. And the fact that I can be quite easily contented with a little has nothing whatever to do with what Augustine calls 'humility'; it is rather a question of laziness and of a weak appetite. I know, just as he does, that there is a kind of perfection beyond the ordinary, different from and above all honour and wealth and the goodness of every day. It is, as the Christians say, a 'peace not of this world' and I too should like to find it. If I can be content without it, or with something not quite so good, it is because I am tired and discouraged, not really because I consider myself unworthy of it. It must be, I suppose, that I do not take my sins seriously enough. I was ashamed of myself, certainly, when for the second time I fell a victim to that evil passion for blood which is excited by the gladiators, and I know too that it was through no goodness and no strength of my own that I am now completely free from it. I regard that freedom as a gift to me from God's mercy. Now, however, that I am free, I cannot honestly say that I am greatly troubled by the thought of any other sins of my own, though, so far as I can understand the Christian preachers, I ought to be conscious of these every day. I do not think that I am good, but I do not think that I am particularly bad either.

And so I am much less humble than Augustine, who, being

better than I am in every way, genuinely believes that what he calls his habitual sin has made him unworthy and incapable of the highest happiness and the most profound peace. I, in seeking a satisfaction lower than the highest, might be happy in a modest way, finding my weariness and dissatisfaction relieved. But he, forgoing the best because of a real and genuine sense of his unworthiness, could, I think, never be happy and, however glorious his life might be, could never, as I could, forget that other state of beatitude which he might perhaps have reached.

Again I thought of Praetextatus and of how in his epitaph his widow, after listing all the honours with which his great and good life had been rewarded, had added the words 'But these were nothing'. No doubt Praetextatus would have agreed with her and it may be that the very greatness of his life was founded on his sense of a security in another life beyond the stars in which the titles and honours and wealth of this world are meaningless. In this acknowledgment Praetextatus also shows a real humility, though it is a different kind of humility from that of Augustine and from that of the Christians in general.

I think in any case that a community such as that planned by Romanianus could not in the end satisfy our desires for either of the two lives—contemplation or action—and it certainly could not reconcile them. And though it was not precisely because of this point that we finally decided to abandon the project, we were all beginning to see that in cutting ourselves off from the world and devoting our whole lives to the search for truth in the manner recommended by Romanianus we would really be acquiring very little that was not available to us already. For none of us except Romanianus believed in his heart that friendship and philosophy, admirable as they are, are capable of giving us the peace and exaltation which we desire. We have studied philosophy for years and have found that, if it leads us anywhere, it leads us in a direction rather away from itself. And though it is natural sometimes to feel an impulse to withdraw from a world that seems to us cruel, ponderous, brutish and irrational, Ventidius is right in pointing out that, do what we may, it is of this world that we are part. I think that, with the exception of Romanianus, all of us were becoming increasingly conscious of something lacking in the plan and that what was lacking was the element of reality. We were being invited, it seemed, to beguile ourselves by playing at being exceptional when we were not this at all. And it was in a way appropriate that in the end the whole scheme broke down on difficulties so eminently practical.

We had often in our discussions argued for or against the presence of women in our community and on the whole the arguments were of an inconclusive nature. It was easy enough for both sides to produce examples of great and wise men who either had or had not encouraged chastity as a means to wisdom and virtue. I myself was undecided on the point. Others were in favour of imitating the Pythagoreans and the Christian priests by taking vows of celibacy. Augustine and Romanianus and others too were strongly in favour of marriage, though there was some divergency of opinion as to whether it would be either practical or desirable for the wives to take part in our philosophical discussions. Romanianus rather surprised me by declaring with confidence that his own wife would be both able and willing to do so. I had often met her in Africa and had imagined (as it turned out, rightly) that her interests were chiefly social. Augustine was scarcely in a position to speak for his future wife, who was still a child, and would be little more than a child when he married her. He did, however, mention the extraordinary intelligence and precosity of his son Adeodatus who, now at the age of sixteen or seventeen, was certainly fully able to take part in any studies which we might make. Indeed he is always surprising us by his intelligence and charming us by his gentleness. Just now he is, I can see, extremely unhappy, since, much as he loves both Augustine and Monnica, he misses his mother. He was keenly aware of her distress when she left and of his father's distress too; but he contrives to conceal his own unhappiness, or at least to make no show of it, and he does this, I am sure, because, knowing or feeling that Augustine's misery is even greater than his own, he is noble and unselfish enough to want to help him rather than, by giving way to his own sorrow, to increase his father's grief. But on this painful subject, if I write at all, I shall write later. At this time probably Augustine and myself were the only people who had any idea of what the boy was going through. Outwardly he was behaving almost normally. His natural good manners are such that only those who knew him very well might have observed that in these talks with Romanianus he was not, in fact, very interested.

Indeed as the discussions went on and on I myself often found my attention wandering and I think it was only the extraordinary energy and enthusiasm of Romanianus himself which prevented others from feeling in the same way. Certainly it was Romanianus who was the most upset when the scheme had to be abandoned. Others—including, as I now know, Augustine—could not help feeling in a way relieved.

For there was one day when we came round to Romanianus' house and found him strangely distraught. His face was pale and he had taken less than his usual trouble with his dress. To our inquiries about his health he answered absent-mindedly and would scarcely speak at all until we were all assembled. Then, without any introduction, he stated (and there was real misery in his voice): 'Today I have to face the hardest decision of my life.'

He went on to explain that he had just received a letter from Africa in which his wife had written to him with regard to his future plans, of which he had been keeping her informed. Her attitude, which was made perfectly clear, had surprised and shocked him and he read us extracts from the letter, including some passages of a rather intimate nature which were really intended only for himself. She began by begging him in the name of all the pleasure and innocent delights which they had enjoyed together to give up a course of action which seemed to her so heartless, cruel, selfish, irresponsible and above all, abysmally stupid. 'I should have thought', she wrote, 'that by this time your own good sense, if not your love for me, would have enabled you to see the folly of what you are doing. Admittedly you are not very intelligent and, whatever you imagine, you are certainly not a great thinker. But at least you are a gentleman and up to now have shown a certain amount of common sense. No doubt some of your friends are more intelligent than you are, but is there a single one of them who has the faintest idea of how to run his life happily and successfully? Even Augustine, about whom you talk so much, is without any kind of stability. He is always changing his religion or his mistress or both. Thanks largely to you, he now has a very good job and, by what you say, he cannot even be satisfied with that. Do you really imagine that, after deserting your wife and ruining your family, you can really be happy with that crowd of conceited young men who seem to think that they are too good for their parents and their friends and the world in general? I wouldn't object to you becoming a Christian, or something respectable. But playing at philosophers! You are like children, and if you weren't so cruel you would make me laugh.'

Then, after a few tender passages, she announced her firm intention of immediately instituting proceedings for divorce unless she received a promise from her husband to return to Africa and give up his plan altogether.

After he had finished reading Romanianus looked round the group of us. His face seemed to show at once dismay, astonishment and apprehension. He spread his hands and spoke jerkily as though he were gasping for air. 'How can she use such words? I loved her. I still love her. How can she be so unreasonable?'

There was something pathetic in his awkward gestures and his uncontrolled voice. Augustine smiled at him and it occurred to me that this was one of the very few times I had seen him smile since Lucilla went away. 'She may be unreasonable,' he said, 'but she is perfectly natural. And everything she says about me is true.'

At first Romanianus looked as though he were about to dispute this statement. Then he seemed to brush it aside and turned to us, speaking now more firmly. 'My friends,' he said, 'you all know how much this community which we have been planning means to me and some of you know how much my wife meant to me too. She still means very much to me, even though it is evident now that we have failed to understand each other. But now I have to choose between her and the future which we have planned and I need your advice. For this has been a great shock to me. I was ready enough to give up my property, or rather to use it not for the honour of myself and of our province, but wisely and in the pursuit of wisdom. But it is harder to give up the affections of the body and the mind. Nevertheless I am prepared to do so, if you can whole-heartedly assure me that this is what you want me to do and what I ought to do.'

As he paused, waiting for a reply, I became sharply aware of what, probably, I had known for some time—that, with all his generosity and high-mindedness and loyalty to us, Romanianus would be acting both stupidly and cruelly if he were to sacrifice his real and natural affections for a scheme so nebulous and, in spite of its superficial attractions, so fundamentally baseless and unreal as that which we had been considering for all these weeks. And it soon became evident that nearly all the rest of us felt very much as I did. Those of us who had wives probably knew, or suspected, that their attitudes were or would be similar to that of the wife of Romanianus. Some owned as much, others argued from more general grounds, such as the duty to maintain and protect the structure of the family. There was no one who encouraged Romanianus to give up his wife and—what was at the same time pathetic and amusing—it soon became evident that

Romanianus himself was becoming increasingly relieved and pleased by the advice he was receiving. And indeed we were all behaving as though we were awaking from a dream.

Indeed the only one of us who showed anything more than or widely different from relief was Augustine. Certainly he, too, had advised Romanianus to do as his wife asked him to do and he had perhaps made things easier for him, partly by the authority he had over him and partly by promising to supervise the studies of his son, Licentius, if he left him behind in Milan. Augustine had also seen at least as clearly as I that what we had aimed to pursue was still the shadow and not the substance of wisdom. But on the way back to our lodging he was thoughtful, silent and depressed. He spoke only once and said, 'The impulse of Romanianus was right and pure. But it was towards the wrong thing. Oh, when shall we both know what is right to do and be able to do it?' There was agony in his voice and this agony, long present, is increasing. I feel that something will be born of it, but I do not know what or when.

V

Today I looked back over what I last wrote in these notebooks. It all seems a long time ago and indeed some considerable time has passed since Romanianus returned to Africa and we all, as it were by mutual consent, abandoned any further discussion of his plan, which had seemed at first so attractive and was so soon discovered to be not only impractical but not even desirable. I see now that, when I was writing at such length about this incident, I must have been not so much interested in it for itself as attempting to distract my mind from what at the time was really moving me—the agony of spirit through which Augustine was passing during those first months after Lucilla went away.

The intensity of this agony went beyond anything which I or Nebridius or, I think, Monnica could fully understand; and the fact that it was, on the whole, fairly well concealed from others made it the more alarming. In spite of very many sleepless nights, he never interrupted his work for a single day. He joined in conversation when it was required of him and I often heard people remark on the extraordinary fervour, brilliance and wit which he showed on these occasions, although Nebridius and I could see well enough, and with pain, that he was not in the least occupied with what he was saying but was merely allowing his memory and intellect to suggest and combine ideas, brilliantly perhaps, but purely automatically. He himself, his real and vivid personality, was not there at all and the well-chosen words and stimulating ideas seemed to us rather a reminder of his absence than his own utterance.

Monnica herself who had, presumably, obtained what she had wanted and what she believed to be good for him, was, for the first time in my experience, doubtful as to whether she had used her influence wisely. She even went so far as to attempt to justify herself to Nebridius and me and to seek our help and support. We were not able to afford much, for we were as distressed as she was about the condition of our friend and equally uncertain as to how best his pain could be cured or alleviated. Perhaps we were of some comfort to her by the mere fact that we did recognize the sincerity of her motives in what she had done—a thing which, I believe, she was beginning to question herself; for she may well have been conscious that among her feelings with regard to Lucilla had been a feeling of jealousy, and for this she doubtless blamed herself, even though in the main her actions had certainly been determined by what she believed was right and good.

241

For years she had prayed every day that Augustine might become whole-heartedly a baptized Christian and now she can see as clearly as we can that this is what he himself wants to be able to do. She knows too that in the Christian Church, though extra-marital relationships are tolerated, they are not approved and that Augustine could never consider himself fit for baptism unless he felt that he could properly fulfil the obligations which he was taking up.

Augustine himself and Lucilla also had thought, or had imagined that they thought, along the same lines. They had felt, as was natural, sad at the prospect of parting from each other; but they had also felt, and largely, I should think, owing to the influence of Monnica, a certain exultation in the sacrifice which they were making. This feeling was certainly more marked and more consistent in Lucilla than in Augustine. She had convinced herself, or been convinced by Monnica, that she was sacrificing her own pleasure for Augustine's good and she was not careful to inquire whether this good was the health of his soul or merely his future success in the world and in his profession. It was sufficient to her to believe that she was doing something of great value for him; for years her life had been bound up with his and she had scarcely given a thought to anything except him, their child and, at regular intervals, her religion. Now that she was leaving him and her child, there was nothing left to her except her religion and it seemed natural and inevitable for her to choose, as she had done, to enter a religious community with other women. Not being used to analysing her thought, she had probably never inquired of herself whether her love for Augustine was stronger than her love for God. It would be wrong to say this or to think this, and so no doubt the very idea of such a comparison had never crossed her mind. And so, in perhaps a rather superficial sense, once she had taken the first step her way was plain.

Augustine had admired her for her simplicity and her single-mindedness, conscious as he was of the complexity of his own mind and of how his desires, more intense than hers, were also more dissipated and, though with every satisfaction in view, never satisfied. For she had been thoughtlessly and naturally happy with him, while with him thought had constantly interrupted happiness. It sometimes seems to me that for everything he does, except for the simplest acts of kindness, he contrives to find some reason to blame himself. And so in this case, while he undoubtedly accepted his mother's view and the view of the Church that his irregular connection with Lucilla was, if not a sin, a serious defect and that it was his duty to do as his mother, his future parents-in-law and Lucilla herself, as it seemed, demanded, he was still uncertain whether he was acting from the right motives and could not help contrasting the completeness of the sacrifice which Lucilla was making with the incompleteness of his own. It seemed to him that she was acting purely for the love of God, whereas in his own case he was aware too of brilliant prospects in front of him and also of the continuance, after a certain interval, of those sexual pleasures in which he was so deeply involved. I think that the thought that there would have to be an interval at all was, in a sense, some consolation to him, though in the end he changed his mind about this.

All this I have learnt from frequent conversations with him and from my own conjectures, though who indeed could ever venture to suppose that he fully understands the mind even of his dearest friend or even his own mind?

As for Lucilla, almost up to the very end she appeared (though I know she was not) calm and there seemed to be much less constraint in her behaviour than there was in that of Augustine. When, as sometimes happened, she discussed her future plan with Monnica, one would have said that she was actually enjoying this, though I can see now that what enjoyment she did get from these talks was merely a kind of make-believe, a distraction from the present which all the time she was finding more and more unbearable. It was to lighten her present real load that she was attempting to pack some reality into the empty and imagined future. Augustine never listened to these discussions, always (and I think she was glad of this) finding some excuse to absent himself. Nebridius and I would occasionally take some part in them, but, as we told each other later, we often felt as though we were acting in some play.

Only once in my presence did Lucilla show what the real state of her mind was and this was on one of the very rare occasions when, during her last few days in Milan, I found her alone. I had come to offer to escort her to the seaport from which she was to embark for Africa with a party of other women, a few of whom were, like her, to enter religious communities there. I knew, though I had not inquired, that it would be too painful both for her and for Augustine if he were to go with her, and I had imagined that, since she had known me for so long, my company would not be unwelcome and that I would be able, in any case, to be of some help when she was travelling.

As I made my suggestion she was standing by a table on which she had been arranging some flowers. She began to thank me, speaking somewhat timidly, though with evident gratitude. She was explaining that everything had been arranged, that she was to travel in a carriage with two ladies, friends of Monnica with whom she had often been engaged in various kinds of charitable work in Milan. She was trying to speak calmly, but she was speaking with difficulty and I could see the tears rising to her eyes. Distressed myself, I smiled at her and stretched out a hand. She took my hand in both of hers and raised it to her lips. 'Oh, Alypius,' she said, 'you are so good.' She too attempted to smile and began to pronounce the words 'I shall miss you'. But now her voice was choking and the tears were flooding over her eyelids. She fell into my arms and began to cover my face with kisses. I too kissed her wet face and she pressed her body more tightly against mine, rubbing her breasts against my chest. Then, with one arm still about my waist she raised the other to my head, twined her fingers in my hair and pulled down my head to her, kissing me over and over again on the eyes and lips. She was moaning like some wounded animal. It was as though she was passionately in love with me and that I had come back from some long journey.

I knew, of course, that this was not the case. What she was embracing in me was some kind of an embodiment of the past which she was leaving; or perhaps I was serving as a substitute for Augustine, to whom she could not bear now to show the real agony that she felt.

Soon she relaxed and I led her to a couch that was set against the wall. Here she let her head fall upon my shoulder and her tears began to flow quietly and unchecked. I could do nothing but support her and wait until she found whatever relief they could afford. For I could see that they were affording her relief, and now—while her head lay on my shoulder and, for a few moments at least, she was able to feel, however unhappy, protected and unrestrained—I pitied, loved and respected her more than ever. The wild embraces and the kisses which a moment previously she had showered upon me, and which in any other circumstances would have seemed lascivious, had, of course, not shocked nor, oddly enough, surprised me. Her small cries, her convulsive movements had been those of an animal, but of an animal who was also human, and of a human animal trapped, desperate and in pain, unable to express itself except in the agitation of limbs, lips, teeth and eyes. But now in the tranquillity of her weeping, in her very abjection, she had gained in dignity. She was not happy, but what was discordant, exacerbating and tumultuous in her was momentarily in abeyance. She was finding somehow in me some kind of temporary security, though what indeed had I to offer her except my pity and my love? Her tears now seemed to be prompted not so much by the real and precise details of her own agony and dissatisfaction, but rather to be expressing a general and universal sorrow in which she, I, Augustine and, one might almost say, all men shared.

245

I wished that she could have gone on weeping. Gradually, however, her tears came more slowly. She sobbed once or twice, raised a hand to her eyes and began to draw away from me. Her body was still relaxed and this weeping had helped her, but now, relieved as she was, she was also bracing herself for a return to actuality and self from the peace which she had found in the forgetfulness of her sorrow.

She moved away from me, sat up and, still wiping her eyes, smiled at me gently. 'I am sorry,' she said, speaking as a child might speak; and then she took one of my hands and raised it to her lips. I found that there were tears in my eyes too. What was there to say? I too was sorry, but my sorrow was not the same as hers. I took her other hand in mine and for some moments we sat in silence. Then, not looking at me, but rather as though she were speaking to herself, she said, 'Dear Alypius'. It seemed that she was about to go on speaking, perhaps wanting to make me promise to give more than usual attention to Augustine after she had gone (though she would have known that such a request was unnecessary); or perhaps she was simply recalling to herself times in the past when we had been happy. But her lips began to quiver and she said nothing. She gently disengaged her hand from mine, kissed me on the forehead and left the room. I never saw her again by herself.

Nor was it for many weeks after she had gone that Augustine found it possible to speak to me or to Nebridius about her. If it ever became necessary for him to mention her name, he would hurry over the syllables as though each one of them, however casually pronounced, were inflicting a sharp pain upon him. During this time he seemed to avoid the company of his mother and even of Adeodatus except when he was supervising his studies. With Nebridius and me he would engage in conversations on religious or philosophical subjects, and sometimes he seemed to find relief in these, particularly, I think when we were discussing the Letters of the Apostle Paul, whom he admires and reveres more than any other of the

246

Christian writers. I often noticed that, during the reading of certain passages, he would become intensely moved and I have prayed that his emotion might break out in tears and so relieve the tension in which he was living. This never happened, and yet it is true that in these readings of the Scriptures he was more nearly himself than when our conversation was concerned with philosophy, literature or sciences. On those subjects, as I have already written, he spoke brilliantly, lucidly and even wittily, but spoke like some ghost whose substance was not in the room at all. Both Nebridius and I wished that he, like most men do, could drug his mind with wine and so escape temporarily from the pain of which he was, as we could see, always conscious. But he has never had any appetite for wine and during this time drank less than ever. He has always however had a liking for food and used often to joke about it, saying that, unless he kept it under the strictest control (as indeed he does), neither his mind nor his body would be able to function for long. Now, however, he began to eat enormous quantities of food. Monnica was at first pleased with this. Like most women she appears to believe that in all cases of sickness and depression an excess of food is, at least with men, a kind of palliative. Soon, however, even she became alarmed when it appeared that he was eating automatically and, as it were, compulsively, without the least idea of what it was that was set before him. Nor did those huge meals have, so far as one could see, the slightest effect on him. After they were over he would proceed directly to work, with no sign of drowsiness or incapacity. Like most people, he had been in the habit of resting in the afternoon, usually with Lucilla; but now he went straight from the table to the books which he was using in preparation for his lectures. After a week or two he suddenly began to eat normally again, or rather frugally. He seemed not to be conscious that previously he had been eating three or four times the amounts to which he was accustomed.

And so, very gradually and almost imperceptibly, some of the strain began to disappear from his face and manner; finally, but not till more than a month had passed, he began to speak again, somewhat as he used to speak, to Nebridius and me. But I think that he was speaking rather for our peace of mind than for his own. He was distressed by our distress and blamed himself as the cause of it. This, however, was at least like himself and we were glad that he was able to speak at all. He owned, what was obvious, that he felt as though a part of himself had been forcibly removed. We attempted to console him with the usual platitudes concerning the healing effects of time. These commonplaces are true, but singularly unhelpful to those who are actually suffering, and he might well have resented hearing them from us. Instead he acknowledged their truth, only adding, 'I have deserved my pain, but how has Lucilla deserved hers? She has chosen what is good. I remain just as I was, hungry for what I do not want.'

Then, and since then, he spoke as we have often heard him speak before, though with, if possible, an even greater intensity. He evidently knew that Lucilla had suffered and was suffering as much as he was, but he was still convinced that what had happened was right and that she, if not himself, had become free and, in the end, capable of happiness. But he saw himself even in her absence bound down by the fetters of his desires. He wanted with his whole heart to devote himself to the service and the enjoyment of the God of whose existence and nature he was now assured. Yet he found that in fact his whole heart was not involved. 'I know', he would say, 'where I want to be, and yet I cannot go there. I know the worthlessness of riches and honours and I know not only the worthlessness, but the uncleanness and dreadful dominance of my habitual pleasures. Yet it is those that I cannot give up. I cannot say to myself, "Never again. Never any more shall I be able to do this or that." And the "this" or "that" of which I think is nothing beautiful. For pure love is without desire and is all the more intense for being so. We love the person not for himself or herself but in God and for God, with no frenzy or grasping or impatience, making no demands. Such love is free and only bounded by the boundless. I can imagine it and indeed I almost know it. And then, just when it seems that light is all round me and my soul is opening her eyes, these thoughts and images, all fleshly, gross, disgusting and all powerful and intense, throng over my sight like buzzing flies and I say to myself, "Not yet. Not yet. Later. But it would be impossible just now." And so I am swept away from what I know that I want towards what I despise and loathe but cannot be without.'

Sometimes when he spoke in this way I would remind him of my own experience when, for the second time, I found myself irresistibly compelled towards the blood and squalor of the arena and all the time had hated and despised myself for doing or, as it seemed, being forced to do what I did. And I pointed out how much worse was my position than his now; for there can be nothing at all to be said for taking a delight in cruelty and brutality, whereas the pleasures of sex are normal and necessary indeed and, as the Church itself teaches, can be sanctified.

Nebridius would support me in these arguments. Both of us, I think, were perhaps more interested in alleviating our friend's distress than in the arguments themselves. Nor did they have much effect on him. 'You do not see', he would say, 'what is in my mind. There is nothing normal and nothing that could be sanctified in my imaginations. They are as abnormal, as brutish and as overwhelming as the lust for blood in the arena. Indeed these two lusts may be different aspects of the same evil. Many people, indeed, may be driven wild and senseless by them, but even if everyone was, that would not make them good.'

But he would listen carefully to whatever I could tell him (and it was not much) about how I had suddenly and almost unaccountably lost all desire for these cruel pleasures and how my liberation had seemed to me to have come from outside myself, since all my self-disgust and all my efforts to control myself had been wholly ineffective.

It is difficult to say whether these discussions, inconclusive as they were, were of any help to him. It was no doubt good for him to be able to talk at all and certainly he began gradually to relax from the extreme agony of those first weeks after Lucilla's departure. No doubt he was aided, too, by the mere passage of time and, perhaps more importantly, by his growing devotion to and fervour for the Christian Church. It was at this time he began to see a lot of Simplicianus, a man known for his great piety and learning and indeed the one who had received Ambrose into the Church and whom Ambrose himself always treated with the utmost respect and affection. It is Augustine's natural diffidence and shyness, I think, which have prevented him from becoming intimate with Ambrose himself. His admiration for him is unbounded, and he and I and Nebridius have on several occasions visited him during the few hours of the day which he sets aside for rest and when he is willing to talk to anyone who needs his advice. But sometimes we have found him reading and have hesitated to interrupt the time of recreation which he so much needs; and at other times he has been listening kindly and politely to various complaints or requests of a very trivial character, and again Augustine has shrunk from taking up the bishop's time and energy by intruding his own problems upon him. And so we have either slipped out of the room quietly and unnoticed, or else merely exchanged greetings before going away.

It seems, however, that Augustine has been able to open his heart more fully to Simplicianus, who is an old man with few administrative duties and who, with his great knowledge of philosophy, and his long experience of the Christian Church both in Rome and Milan and his knowledge of and sympathy with human nature, seems perfectly adapted to help one who, like Augustine, is both eager and diffident, anxious to be instructed and humble, yet meticulous in his examination of every fact and argument.

Augustine has been impressed by the learning of Simplicianus, but even more so by his kindness, his certainty and the stories which, from his own experience, he can tell of men whose lives have been utterly changed and whose eyes opened by conversion to the Christian faith. Simplicianus' memory goes back to the time of the Emperor Julian and he speaks with great pride and affection of those who remained steadfast then or were actually converted, often men of power, fame and eloquence like the great orator in Rome, Victorinus, the translator of the Neo-Platonic books into Latin and one of the most learned men of his day, who chose this moment of persecution to declare openly that long study had convinced him of the truth of the Christian religion and that, if he expected Christ to accept him in front of the angels, it was his plain duty not to deny Christ before men or even to dissimulate, for any reason of advantage or expedience or consideration of friends, the conviction that he held. Simplicianus told these stories easily and naturally, not over-emphasizing the heroism that was shown by Victorinus and others and not condemning outright those many people who, to suit the times, had changed their faith. It was as though he regarded it as admirable but also natural that good men with firm convictions should behave with heroism and that those who were weaker should act weakly.

Augustine is immensely moved by these stories. It is evident to Nebridius and me, and probably to Simplicianus, that it is just such a sacrifice as that of Victorinus that he himself is longing to make. Yet he is too honest to do or to attempt to do such a thing unless he can do it with utter and entire conviction—something beyond the intellectual conviction which he has already and something which would have no trace of that self-imposed abnegation which is often merely a cloak for real weakness or suppressed pride.

So this struggle, more clearly defined, I suppose, than it

used to be, but still not resolved, goes on inside him with now greater and now less stress and intensity. I myself feel involved in it and so, I think, does Nebridius. We feel more than spectators. It is rather as though Augustine were acting out for us a struggle in which we too are engaged, though we understand it more dimly and feel its implications less intensely than he does.

For though we understand well many of his thoughts and actions, he will still surprise us. Just recently, for instance, he has acquired another mistress—not a girl whom he will bring to the house, but one whom he visits frequently, though in a somewhat clandestine manner. I had imagined that having taken this step he would be overwhelmed with guilt and dismay and no doubt he does feel both of these. Yet he feels them with less intensity than I might have expected. What he feels most, perhaps, is a kind of disappointment. 'What I do', he said to me, 'is not so bad as what I imagine.'

He was speaking with great bitterness and with a strange kind of humility. For no reason that I can define, his words or the tone of his voice made me feel hopeful, but I scarcely know for what I hope.

VI

It was two days ago that Ponticianus came to see us and within two hours of his departure everything in our life has changed. Yet when he came and when he left neither of us knew, neither of us had the least idea, what would happen and what was happening. Since then we have talked it over between ourselves and with Monnica, recalling each detail and recalling everything, even what was at the time most painful and tempestuous, with joy and calm and wonder. It seems to us that neither of us has done anything to deserve this happy state, nor was there anything in the events of those few hours which could in itself be said to have caused or precipitated it. No doubt I, without Augustine, should never have reached it; yet he himself had no knowledge of what precisely was taking place within him. We must be the same people and yet everything has changed and what we see is what we always wanted to see and could never see and yet which, it now seems to us, must always have been clearly and instantly visible if we had opened our eyes. Now we wonder what prevented us from doing what we so much longed to do. Augustine says that in his case it was pride and lust. With me I think it must have been something more like timidity and also a kind of pride, an unwillingness wholly to surrender myself to so much love and such profound simplicity.

How useless and unnecessary now seem to me all those words which I have written since I first came to Rome! How could I ever have imagined that by groping so haphazardly in so large a space and so great a darkness I could ever have discovered anything, particularly when I did not even know what it was that I was so desperately searching for? All that I have succeeded in recording are indications of my own incapacity and perhaps of the incapacity of everyone who, like me and my friends, has ever fancied himself able to learn without submission and to know without loving. Nor can I now find words to describe our peace. All I can do is to set down, while it is still fresh in my memory, an account of words and gestures, not very remarkable in themselves or in their sequence and yet which, unaccountably but wonderfully and, as we believe, divinely, led us to this perfect satisfaction. After this I shall never have the need or the wish to write further of the self which I have lost and found.

That morning our condition, so far as we could tell, was

the same as it had been for so long. Indeed we seemed almost to be becoming used, I in a kind of lethargy and Augustine in a more controlled despair, to the imperfect satisfaction of our desire for wisdom, understanding and clarity. Nebridius had been in the same state, though he was not with us then and still has not returned from a visit he has had to pay to Rome. We were sitting in one of the rooms in our house overlooking the garden. Augustine was reading and I was looking out at the trees and the grass still covered with dew and glistening in the early spring sun. We were surprised to have a caller at this hour and when Ponticianus came into the room I did not at first recognize him. In fact he is a little older than Augustine and, though I had known him in Carthage, I had only known him slightly. His manner had changed too. I remembered him as a gay and somewhat irresponsible young man; now he carried himself with great dignity, as one used to being treated with respect and deserving it. He had only recently heard, he told us, that we were in Milan and had come to renew an old acquaintanceship. And so we began to talk, in an ordinary enough way, about our youth in Carthage and about our lives at present. Ponticianus had just returned to Milan from an embassy to the East. He was now an important official at the emperor's court and we congratulated him on his successful career. He accepted our congratulations gracefully and politely but showed no particular enthusiasm with regard to the power and influence which he must have, and quickly went on to ask us about ourselves. He was easy and pleasant to talk with and before long we were making arrangements to meet again. Then, as the conversation became more relaxed, Ponticianus happened to pick up the book which Augustine had been reading and which was still open on the table. It was a copy of the Letters of the Apostle Paul and when he had glanced at it his expression changed in a remarkable way. He appeared to be first incredulous and then strangely pleased. He smiled first at Augustine and then at me and then said simply and with great sincerity, 'I did not expect it, but how glad I am to find you reading that book!'

Augustine blushed. It would occur to him, of course, that Ponticianus would remember him in the days when he had been a Manichaean and a hostile critic of all the Christian writing which he had read. I believe that Ponticianus himself, like me and others, had come under his influence at that time. So it was at first with some embarrassment that Augustine began to speak of his admiration for Paul, though he was soon speaking naturally and with his usual eloquent enthusiasm.

Ponticianus listened gravely and intently, evidently delighted with what was being said. He told us that he himself had been for a long time now a baptized Christian and somehow from this point our conversation became more intimate, natural and, as it were, trustful than it had been before. I cannot remember how it was that he came to tell us of those Christian communities in the deserts of Egypt which he had visited himself. He was surprised that we knew so little about them and was quite astonished to find that we had never heard the name of the monk Anthony who had lived almost a hundred years ago and who throughout the East, and according to Ponticianus, in the West too, was venerated as the perfect example of the hermitical life. He told us how Anthony, as a young and rich man, had received, like Paul and the other Apostles, a direct call from God. He had entered a church while the gospel was being read and had heard, as though the words were (and indeed they were) directed to him personally, the sentence: 'Go and sell that thou hast, and give to the poor, and thou shalt have treasure in heaven: and come and follow me.' And so in perfect obedience and with no hesitation he had gone to his home, sold all his possessions and given the proceeds to the poor, the widows and the orphans, left his sister in a Christian home for virgins and had then withdrawn for twenty years entirely from the world, first to the tombs outside his village and then to a ruined fort in the hills where food was brought to him once every six months. Thousands of disciples had flocked to see him and to watch him at his prayers and no doubt it was for their sakes that after these twenty years of his youth and middle age he came down from the hill-top and spent six years in organizing those first communities of monks and virgins, which have now so greatly increased in number. He then retired still further into the wilderness and there in the remote deserts remained until his death, which took place when he was more than a hundred years old.

As I listened to the story told by Ponticianus I was fascinated by all that I heard and hung upon his words so that I did not observe what effect they were having on Augustine. All I noticed was that Augustine had buried his face in his hands and I imagined that he was doing this, as he often does, to achieve greater concentration while listening. And so Ponticianus was addressing himself more particularly to me since I was following him with my eyes and he could see how moved I was by what he was saying.

He was telling me of some of the miracles performed by Anthony and I was still listening entranced, when he happened to glance towards Augustine and suddenly, as though in alarm, broke off his narration. Augustine had taken his hands away from his face. I too was alarmed by its expression which seemed to show extreme pain and at the same time a wild excitement, as though he were in some high fever. His lips were trembling, and he kept clenching and unclenching his hands.

Ponticianus spoke to him kindly. 'Am I upsetting you or tiring you?' he asked. 'Forgive me. Perhaps you are not well.'

Augustine did his best to speak normally, but his lips still trembled when he attempted to smile. I knew that he was deeply moved and expected to see tears in his eyes, but they were hard and desperate. 'No, my friend,' he said, 'it is I whom you must forgive. It was just when you were speaking

256

of Anthony leaving everything.' He paused, strangely at a loss for words and then repeated, 'Leaving everything.' His voice was choking, yet with a great effort he seemed to gain control of himself and smiled more naturally. 'Please go on,' he said.

Ponticianus looked at him gravely and sympathetically. Clearly he wished to comply and at the same time was anxious by some change in the conversation or in its tone to allow Augustine to grow calmer. 'I myself,' he said, 'have had an experience which might interest you. It concerns some friends of mine who are now, to the best of my belief, good and holy men. Better men, certainly, than I am. And, in an indirect way, it was Anthony who was responsible for the change in them. But perhaps I have been talking too long already?'

Augustine shook his head. He was still agitated, but he had regained some of his control. Both he and I urged Ponticianus to continue. As he spoke I watched my friend more closely and I doubt whether anyone who knew him less well than I do could have seen how deep and agonizing was the impression being made on him by what he was hearing. Indeed I myself did not fully realize its effect on him till afterwards. He was, I think, while listening intently and absorbing every word, somehow managing to suppress and control the feelings which all the time they were arousing and, as he suppressed them, so they gathered weight and force.

Ponticianus was telling us of how some years ago he had been in attendance on the emperor who at that time had his court at Trèves and was holding the chariot races there. One day he and three friends, all attached to the court, had gone for a walk in the gardens near the city walls. After a time they had separated into two groups, Ponticianus and one friend going one way and the other two another. In the evening, when it was time to return to the city, Ponticianus and his companion had looked for some time for the other two; they knew the direction in which they had gone, but could see

nothing of them and were on the point of returning alone
when they happened to look inside a small hut set back from
one of the paths and there they found their friends, both upon
their knees and praying. When interrupted, they had told
Ponticianus and the other officer exactly what had happened.
'And what was extraordinary', Ponticianus at this point
commented to us, 'was that everything they said, strange as it
was, seemed perfectly natural.'

It appeared that this hut provided shelter for a small community of Christians who had decided to retire from the
world, and live their lives in prayer and meditation. Ponticianus' friends had entered it for no purpose that they could
name and had found it deserted. One of the two, again out of
no motive more serious than idle curiosity, had picked up a
book that was lying there and had begun to look through its
pages. It happened to be a Life of Anthony and as he read it
he became more and more absorbed in what he was reading,
so that his companion looked at him in a kind of astonishment
and did not venture to interrupt him. Suddenly he had looked
up and exclaimed, 'What have we been doing with our lives?
Why are we in the imperial service and so proud of it? What
do we expect to gain? The highest we could even hope for
would be to become friends of the emperor himself, and we
know how hard it is to reach that position and how precarious
and dangerous a life we would have even if we did attain it.
Yet now, in a moment, we can instantly give ourselves to the
service of God and become his friends.' Then he turned to
his reading again and a little later looked up and said, 'I myself am entering this service here and now. You may not wish
to join me but you must not try to do anything to dissuade
me. My mind and soul are settled.' And his friend had decided
to stay there with him. As for Ponticianus and the other
officer, they too had made no attempt to alter what had happened. 'Indeed,' Ponticianus said to us, 'we felt sad and
ashamed when we went away after begging our friends to
pray for us. And still I know that they have chosen a better

life than mine and are happier, though I have heard nothing of them since. Or I heard only one thing. Both of them were engaged to girls of good family and connections; and when these girls heard what had happened, they followed the example of their lovers and retired from the world, offering their virginities to God.'

Ponticianus too had been moved by the story he had been telling us and by the effect (though he could not have guessed how great this effect was) that it had had upon Augustine and me. It was perhaps in an endeavour to make the atmosphere more relaxed that he began to speak in general terms. 'And these events,' he said, 'are not isolated, as you may think. They happen every day. One wonders what is going on. In the past people seem to have accepted the world as it was and found hope in it. Now that is no longer true.'

He paused, no doubt expecting one or other of us to make some comment, but if we said anything, it was of no importance and indeed it seemed difficult to speak at all. I imagine that we said the usual polite things when he left, promising to visit us again.

After he had gone Augustine and I looked at each other for a moment in silence. I did not know precisely what I felt, only that my feeling was deep. It was, as usual, Augustine who found words to express something of what was in our hearts, even though his own feelings were stronger, fiercer, more agonizing and more overwhelming than my own. This was evident from the extraordinary pallor of his face, the stiffness of his whole body, the roughness of his voice. He was like a man undergoing torture. As for me, I was already conscious, together with an extreme agitation, of something not quite recognizable, but approaching peace. And then, too, I was alarmed for my friend, for though I have often seen him in moments of mental agony, I had never seen him in a state like this. As he began to speak his eyes were blazing. If a stranger had been present, he would have imagined that we were engaged in a violent and dangerous quarrel. 'Oh

Alypius,' he said, 'look at us! Look at us with all our learning, all our aspirations, our half-knowledge and our half-love! Are we not ashamed? These others of whom we have been hearing quickly and decisively take the lead and we shrink back cowering, timorous, wretched in our terror. And I, bedded and wallowing in the flesh, do not even take one step.'

Some such words as these he spoke, but so incoherently that I can scarcely remember them. Then he turned away and went out into the garden of the house. He snatched up with him, seeming scarcely conscious of what he was doing, the book upon the table. I followed him, disturbed myself and alarmed for him. At any other time I should have taken his arm or made some sign of my affection, but now he was like a creature all on fire and I shrank from touching him, though I was fonder of him than ever.

He went to a bench as far as possible from the house and sat down. I sat with him, still saying nothing. He had told me since that he was glad of my presence and indeed what could I have done but stay beside him? For he was now utterly distraught. When he was silent his face and his limbs seemed to be expressing his fever and he unconscious of what they were doing. His hands would grip at his hair, pulling it; he would rise suddenly to his feet and as suddenly sit down again; his fists would clench and unclench; he would throw out an arm as though in defence or in supplication; and all the time his face was twisted and contorted in pain. Sometimes words would be forced through his lips, words of self-reproach, invocations to God and obscenities too, but he was quite unconscious of what he was saying. Even much later, when he has attempted to explain to me what was then passing through his mind, he has found it impossible to be quite intelligible. It was as though, he says, he was trying desperately to break away from a chain that was always very slightly weakening and yet which never quite broke, and he knew that, unless he could tear himself free then and there, he would be bound down for ever. But this, he says (and I can believe him), is a feeble and remote image for what in reality was taking place.

Suddenly I noticed a slight change in his expression. It had not become calm but it was less tortured and sadder. Again he rose to his feet and this time his movements were less convulsive. He walked away from me and I felt that he now did not want or need my presence by him. I watched him as he walked away slowly to the shade of a fig tree at a little distance from us. Here he flung himself on the ground and I could see his shoulders shaking with sobs as the tears came flowing from his eyes. I was still looking at him with amazement and with pity. It seemed to me that this storm of tears must be helping him and yet I trembled (how unnecessarily) as I wondered in what state of mind he would rise up from the ground.

I saw his body gradually relax and now it lay still. Then he raised himself up on one hand and turned his head in the direction of the wall that surrounded the garden. I could not see his face, but he appeared to be listening intently to some sound that was coming from the other side of the wall. I strained my ears to hear what it was, but could hear nothing.

Suddenly he turned in my direction and I could see that the expression of his face had become normal except that it showed some extraordinary excitement. He came towards me and now he was walking lightly and eagerly. I felt, though without knowing why, a sense of joy and I too somehow became involved in the excitement which lit up his face.

As he looked at me I saw that his eyes were different—no longer tortured and no longer unrecognizing. Yet still he could not speak. He took up the book that was still lying open beside me, turned over as though automatically and unseeingly a few pages and set his finger on a passage which he began to read in silence. As he read his face became transfigured. I have seen it in every mood but I have never seen, nor ever could have imagined, a look and light of such joy. So he stood for a few moments and then turned to speak to me. In his voice was all and more than the old friendliness and love; he was the same person and yet utterly different and I was awed and amazed.

All he told me then was that, when his tears had ceased, he had become aware of a voice, as it were the voice of a child, coming from the other side of the wall and it had seemed to him that this voice had been going on for a long time, so that he was surprised that he had not noticed it before. He had supposed that it had been because he had been in no condition to notice anything. 'I was scarcely even aware of you, Alypius,' he said, smiling, but as though asking and expecting my forgiveness, and with no trace whatever in his face of all that torture and agitation. 'Tell me, did you hear that voice?'

I told him that I had listened and heard nothing. 'I heard it,' he said, and told me that the voice had been saying over and over again: 'Take it and read it. Take it and read it.' This, he had thought, must be some kind of a refrain from a children's game, and he had tried to remember if he had ever heard such a refrain before, going back to his own childhood, and then to times in Carthage, in Rome and in Milan when in idle moments he had listened to children playing in the streets or gardens. But he could remember no occasion when these words had been used. Then it occurred to him that the words were addressed to him. He felt an overwhelming excitement, but no surprise whatever; and he remembered the book lying on the seat beside me, though he was not aware that he himself had brought it there from the house. So he had opened it and his finger had led him to the following words: 'Not in rioting and drunkenness, not in chambering and wantonness, not in strife and envying; but put ye on the Lord Jesus Christ, and make not provisions for the flesh in concupiscence.'

It was unnecessary for him to try to tell me how those words had affected him. I had seen his face already and I knew that he had found what we had so long been looking for.

Until now I had been only dimly aware of what all this

time had been going on in my own mind, since my thoughts had been fully occupied in the agony of my friend. Nor can I tell whether it was what we had heard from Ponticianus or simply the sight of Augustine's torture and of his release from it which now made me more conscious than I had ever been before of my own unhappiness, weakness and indecision. It seemed to me that Augustine, as so often before, was showing me the way and yet in order to follow him I still needed something more. I opened the book at the place where he had been reading and the words on which my eye lighted were enough. They were these: 'Him that is weak in the faith, receive.'

Before I had time to attempt to tell Augustine how these words, so appropriate to my state, had changed everything for me, he had understood. We looked at each other in delight. It was as though we, whose hearts and minds had for so long been so close, were now seeing each other for the first time. We embraced in silence, and as we drew apart, the sky, the trees, the grass, the very walls of the house and twigs of wood upon the ground looked different, swimming in light yet distinct, sharp and beautiful as I had never seen them.

Now in the spring we are waiting until Easter when we shall receive baptism. Then we shall return to Africa and then who can tell what the future will hold for us? We have only begun to know ourselves by knowing that we are neither good, nor wise nor strong and that we shall never be any of these things, but that all around us on every side and around every living and inanimate creature—around Praetextatus and the drunken beggar, the lawyers and my landlord in Rome, Ambrose and Symmachus—extend and call to us the infinite love and the infinite wisdom of God.